Parenting by Grace

Discipline and Spiritual Growth
Parent's Guide

Nashville, Tennessee

ISBN 0-8054-9939-3

Dewey Decimal Classification: 649
Subject Heading: PARENT AND CHILD \ CHILDREN-MANAGEMENT

This book is the text for course CG-0209
in the subject area Home/Family of the Christian Growth Study Plan.

Order additional copies of this book by writing to Customer Service Center, MSN 113;
127 Ninth Avenue, North; Nashville, TN 37234-0113; by calling toll free (800) 458-2772;
by faxing (615) 251-5933; by ordering online at *www.lifeway.com;* by emailing
customerservice@lifeway.com; or by visiting a LifeWay Christian Store.

For information about adult discipleship and family resources, training, and events,
visit our Web site at *www.lifeway.com/discipleplus.*

Printed in the United States of America

LifeWay Press
127 Ninth Avenue, North
Nashville, Tennessee 37234-0151

*As God works through us, we will help people and churches know Jesus Christ
and seek His kingdom by providing biblical solutions that
spiritually transform individuals and cultures.*

The Story of Parenting by Grace

Early in the formation of the 1982-85 Strengthen Families Emphasis, parent enrichment was identified by Southern Baptists as an area of concern. In May, 1981, Doug Anderson, then Family Enrichment Section supervisor, appointed a design team to work in the area of parent enrichment. The team included Harold Bergen, chairperson; SuAnne Bottoms; and Lee Sizemore. Under the direction of Doug Anderson, and later Gary Hauk, this team has brought Parenting by Grace into reality.

In September, 1981, sixteen professionals representing child development, theology, curriculum development, family counseling, pastoral ministries, and pediatric medicine came together to brainstorm areas of parent enrichment. The group included Max Price, Dixie Ruth Crase, Julienne Thomas, Pat Clendinning, Deana Blackburn, Mayhan and Janice Siler, J. Clark Hensley, Howard and Norma Stevens, Dwayne and Beth Cole, Keith Wilkinson, Sybil Waldrop, W. Wayne Grant, Raymond and Pat Bailey, Lee Sizemore, SuAnne Bottoms, Richard Waggener, Doug Anderson, and Harold Bergen.

From this early effort, a design paper was completed in May, 1983, after input was received from several Sunday School Board professionals. It laid the theological foundation for the project and identified the needs and concerns of Southern Baptist parents.

The team then devised an educational model that would be effective in parent enrichment. In February, 1983, they met with LeRoy Ford and Wesley Black to develop an educational model.

Based on the theological concepts and the educational model developed, writers were selected to write the materials for the field test. They included Wesley Black, Carol Bumbalough, Diana Garland, and Judy Latham (see biographical information on page 8). LeRoy Ford attended the writer's conference as educational consultant.

After the field test material was written, the next months were devoted to copy editing, styling, and arranging the materials that leaders would use in conducting the field tests.

In January, 1984, thirty-six Family Ministry state program leaders and approved persons met at Ridgecrest Conference Center, North Carolina, to be trained to conduct the field tests. They included: *Alabama:* Steve Stephens; *Alaska:* Harold Hime; *Arizona:* Steven Dowdle; *California:* Gil Brink, Darrell Adcock, Wally and Lois Rice; *Colorado:* D.G. and Berlee McCoury; *District of Columbia:* Paul Clark, Jr.; *Florida:* Bob and Helen Cook; *Hawaii:* Glenn Harada; *Idaho:* Luman Gilman; *Illinois:* Ed and Kathleen Claybrook; *Iowa:* John Adams; *Kansas:* Dorothy James; *Kentucky:* Vernon Cole; *Louisiana:* Ray Wells; *Maryland:* Jim Osborn, Grovan McClellan, Robert Gerstmyer; *Michigan:* Jack Elliott; *Mississippi:* J. Clark Hensley, Paul Jones, Billy Johnson, George Lee; *Missouri:* Paul Thompson, Kenneth Taylor, Thom Meigs; *Nevada:* Rudy Duett; *New York:* William Dunning; *North Carolina:* Robert Newton; *Oregon:* Charles Purvis; *Oklahoma:* Janet Bradshaw; *South Carolina:* Al Price; *Texas:* Mike Lundy; *Utah:* Guy Ward; *Virginia:* Gwynn Davis, Jr.

After the training and field tests were completed, reports indicated that more than 1800 parents participated in sixty-five events in twenty-seven states. During the summer of 1984, the model was taught during Sunday School and Church Training weeks at Glorieta and Ridgecrest Conference Centers. Nearly 450 people participated in these conferences, bringing the total to 2250 parents participating in field tests.

Research results of the field tests were shared with the team in a meeting in Nashville in August, 1984. An advisory group met in September at Fall Creek Falls State Park, Tennessee, to discuss a church use plan, resources, training, and promotion for this new Southern Baptist Parent Enrichment Program. All of the participants—Janet Bradshaw, Gil Brink, Mike Lundy, D.G. McCoury, Ed Claybrook, Dorothy James, Ray Wells, Al Price, and Steve Stephens—had led the model in one or more churches.

Family Ministry state program leaders met in Nashville in December, 1984, to further refine a direction for leader training and plan a ninety-five-week countdown to launch Parenting by Grace. They met again in April, 1985, at Trinity Pines Conference Center, Texas, to review plans for training parent enrichment leaders to provide input into materials being developed.

In May, 1985, materials were proposed for the initial Parenting by Grace course. You have in your hands one of those pieces. The other is *Parenting by Grace: Discipline and Spiritual Growth Leader's Guide,* the resource piece for conducting this course. Dixie Ruth Crase and Art Criscoe were enlisted as writers for the final material (see biographical information on page 8).

In June, 1986, Parenting by Grace was officially launched at Ridgecrest and Glorieta Conference Centers during Church Training weeks. A network of trainers was established to provide guidance to churches who conduct Parenting by Grace courses.

Parenting by Grace, then, was not developed overnight. A great deal of study, planning, research, and testing was accomplished to bring to you what we believe is a unique and valuable tool for parent enrichment.

How to Use the Parent's Guide

Your *Parenting by Grace: Discipline and Spiritual Growth Parent's Guide* will be a valuable tool for you as you work through this course. Besides reading the material, you will want to complete the learning exercises and parent-child activities throughout the guide. They will prepare you for the group sessions you will participate in as scheduled.

You may have received this guide before attending the introductory session. If so, you should complete the "Introduction" (page 10) before attending and pray about your involvement in the course. If you did not receive the guide early, that's fine. Your leader will share expectations for you and him during the introductory session.

If you will not be attending a group session as a part of your study, it will be imperative that you complete all written work and parent-child activities in order to gain from the course.

The old adage, "You only get out of something whatever you put in" applies to this course. We wish you well on your pilgrimage through Parenting by Grace.

Field Test Writers

Wesley Black, instructor in youth education, Southwestern Baptist Theological Seminary, Ft. Worth, Texas

Carol Bumbalough, freelance writer in the area of youth and children's materials, Nashville, Tennessee

Diana Garland, Social Work Division, Baylor University, Waco, Texas

Judy Latham, children's editor for LifeWay Christian Resources, Nashville, Tennessee

The Writers

Dixie Ruth Crase compiled the content material for *Parenting by Grace: Discipline and Spiritual Growth Parent's Guide*. A native of New Mexico, Dr. Crase is professor of child development at Memphis State University, Memphis, Tennessee. She holds degrees from Eastern New Mexico University, Kansas State University, and Ohio State University.

Dr. Crase and her husband, Dr. Darrell Crase, also a member of the faculty at Memphis State, have a daughter, Amy, who—at the time of this writing—is a freshman at Belmont College, Nashville, Tennessee.

Dr. Crase is a wife, mother, professor of early childhood education, Christian, and an active member of Second Baptist Church, Memphis—characteristics that highly qualified her to compose the content for this first Parenting by Grace course.

Arthur H. Criscoe wrote the interactive learning exercises for *Parenting by Grace: Discipline and Spiritual Growth Parent's Guide*. A native of Alabama, Dr. Criscoe is director of the Discipleship and Family Youth/Children/Preschool Department of LifeWay Christian Resources, Nashville, Tennessee. He holds degrees from Samford University and Southwestern Baptist Theological Seminary. He has done additional study at Texas Christian University, the Catholic University of America, the University of South Carolina, and the University of Michigan.

While a doctoral student at Southwestern Seminary, Dr. Criscoe studied with Dr. LeRoy Ford, a leader in the development of interactive learning. Dr. Criscoe and Dr. Ford have joined together to lead conferences in training writers in affective learning techniques.

Dr. Criscoe has written several books, interactive study guides for videos, teaching workbooks for Baptist doctrines studies, and has co-authored several Equipping Center modules.

With this background, Dr. Criscoe was well qualified to write the interactive learning exercises for this initial Parenting by Grace course.

Contents

Introduction

Overview

Introduction

Congratulations! You have just taken an important step. You have indicated your interest in continuing to become a better parent. Welcome to Parenting by Grace!

Parenting by Grace is not a new concept. It is as timeless as God's love for mankind. As a specific Southern Baptist program of parent enrichment, Parenting by Grace has a relatively brief but rich history. For more than eight years, Southern Baptist parents and professionals cooperatively researched and studied the concept of Parenting by Grace. Perhaps you are one of the hundreds of parents who participated in field tests throughout the United States. A debt of gratitude is due for each contributor to these materials.

This Parenting by Grace course deals with discipline and spiritual growth. But Parenting by Grace is more than a single course of study. It is a way of life, an attitude that grows from understanding and experiencing God's grace.

Parenting by Grace is a part of the LIFE (Lay Institute for Equipping) learning system. Parenting by Grace and other LIFE courses enable Christians to grow at their own pace and develop skills and competencies in various areas according to their own life goals and spiritual gifts. Each LIFE course includes individual study and on-the-job experience. A weekly seminar or small-group session brings the two together as participants discuss and reflect on their learning.

This introduction explains Parenting by Grace as a concept and as a course and stresses the importance of your commitment to complete the course. The purpose of Parenting by Grace is given, along with an overview of the course. The significance of parenting, trends in parenting, and the needs of parents are discussed. The biblical concept of grace is examined as the foundation of parenting.

The Purpose of Parenting by Grace
Overview of Parenting by Grace
Significance of Parenting
Trends in Parenting
The Needs of Parents
Sharing Needs with Other Parents
Grace—the Foundation of Parenting
Parenting by Grace Presuppositions
Your Commitment to Parenting by Grace
Checkpoint
Reflection and Application
Summary
Looking Ahead

Each lesson has a general goal related to the purpose of Parenting by Grace and also specific learning outcomes.

After completing this introduction, you should have a better understanding of Parenting by Grace as a concept

and as a course. You will be able to—
- describe the purpose of Parenting by Grace;
- state two reasons why parenting is significant;
- list at least three trends in parenting;
- identify two needs you have as a parent;
- define grace;
- explain the role of grace in parenting; and
- make a commitment to complete this course.

The Purpose of Parenting by Grace

The purpose of this course is simple yet profound—to help you become a better parent. Parenting by Grace is designed to help Christian parents understand and exercise the gift of God's grace in parenting. This means to love, affirm, discipline, and guide children to mature, responsible Christian living. Here are some of the ways this course will help you:

- You will gain a better understanding of the role of love and affirmation in parenting.
- You will gain a better understanding of the nature and use of discipline in parenting.
- You will gain a better understanding of the growth and development of your child(ren).
- You will gain a better understanding of the "teachable moment" and how to use it in the parenting process.
- You will gain a better understanding of the importance and role of "modeling" in parenting.
- You will gain a better understanding of how to plan for a regular family time together.
- You will be able to practice the basic principles and guidelines related to the above concepts and areas.

Overview of Parenting by Grace

Parenting by Grace is organized into this introduction and ten lessons. The lessons are divided into five units.
Introduction
Unit One: Grace: God's Gift to Parents and Children
  Lesson 1: Love and Affirmation
  Lesson 2: Discipline and Guidance
Unit Two: Helping Children Grow According to God's Plan
  Lesson 3: Physical, Moral, and Spiritual Development
  Lesson 4: Discipline Grows Children in the Way They Should Go
Unit Three: How to Discipline by Grace
  Lesson 5: Discipline Affirms Appropriate Behavior
  Lesson 6: Discipline Finds Alternatives to Replace Inappropriate Behavior
Unit Four: Applying Grace to Your Parenting
  Lesson 7: Seizing the Teachable Moment
  Lesson 8: Teaching Through Example
Unit Five: Sustaining Grace in Your Parenting
  Lesson 9: Experiencing and Celebrating Family
  Lesson 10: Parents: Sharing and Supporting
This *Parent's Guide* is for you to work through on your own at home, one lesson at a time. The course is designed for a one-hour group session to follow each lesson. Sometimes a group will meet for two hours and cover two lessons. It is important that you complete each lesson before the group meeting.

Each lesson will require several hours of work on your part. Some of this time will be spent reading and working through the lesson. Much of the time will be spent putting into practice what you have learned. We believe the results and dividends you will experience will richly repay you for your investment of work and commitment.

Do not simply read the *Parent's Guide* without completing the activities and assignments. To do so would short-circuit the learning process and deprive you of achieving the learning goals.

Significance of Parenting

Whether you are expecting your first child or first grandchild, you are aware of the importance of parenting. Whether you grew up in a strong, healthy family or a home with major difficulties, you sense the signficance of your parents' influence on your life.

Underline the reasons given in the following paragraphs why parenting is significant.

Why is parenting so important? There are many reasons. Parents are given the first opportunity to influence, guide, and relate to children in all areas of life from spiritual to intellectual. The younger the child, the more easily he can be shaped and influenced by others.

In addition to being the first primary factor shaping children's lives, the parent-child relationship is also one of the most powerful emotional ties experienced by human beings. Surely God planned it so! The initial and continuing influence of parents upon children's development is immeasurable.

Whether your child's latest venture is pulling up and standing alone, riding a bicycle without training wheels, being fitted for braces, practicing for the school play, or going away to college, the daily challenges and rewards of parenthood are obvious. Parenting is one of the most demanding and awesome responsibilities we assume in a lifetime.

State two reasons why parenting is significant. Refer to the preceding paragraphs as needed.

• _____

• _____

Most parents sense the importance of their responsibilities. In fact, a thoughtful consideration of parenting can be almost overwhelming. Most of us are quick to acknowledge our failures as parents. We are the first to recognize we are not perfect.

Good news! Parenting by Grace is not designed to add to your feelings of frustration, failure, or guilt. Parenting by Grace is based on the recognition that as children of God we are parented by grace. In turn, we are charged with offering our children the blessings associated with parenting by grace.

Trends in Parenting

A sensitivity to the significance of parenting leads to an increased awareness of current trends in parenting. The modern media regularly reminds us of—
- the number of teen pregnancies;
- the high divorce rate;
- the increasing number of single parents;
- the percentage of mothers who work outside the home;
- the young children who are regularly cared for by someone other than a family member;
- the latchkey children who get themselves off to school and let themselves into an empty apartment after school;
- the abuse of children, spouses, and the elderly;
- the adolescents who experiment with drugs, alcohol, and sex;
- the prevalence of suicide—even among elementary-age children;
- the young people who drop out and/or run away from home, school, church, society; and
- the young adults who find neither material success nor spiritual happiness and return to the nest from which they were launched.

Examine a current newspaper for trends in parenting. Place a check beside each trend descibed above if you can find a news item or story in the paper concerning that trend.

List what you consider to be the trends in parenting today.

- _____

Are we winning or losing at the all-important game of parenting? Each of us can probably identify with one or more of the preceding descriptors of modern families. Directly or indirectly, our families have felt the influence of an unplanned pregnancy, an alcoholic family member, an overworked parent, an undisciplined preschooler, or a testing adolescent. What challenges these situations present to the best-prepared parents.

The Needs of Parents

Most parents have had little conscious preparation for the highly significant responsibility of parenting. Admittedly, each of us has been parented. Indeed the quality of our own parenting skills is in part a reflection of our parents' strengths and weaknesses. Particularly during times of stress, we tend to return to behaviors and responses with which we are most familiar. All of us are able to identify areas of strengths and areas where we are most needy as parents.

Reflect upon your own needs as a parent. List what you consider to be your two most pressing needs.

- _____

- _____

Whether you look back over certain parenting experiences in your past or look forward to challenges in the future, you are reminded of the complexity of parenthood. One thing is clear. Most of us have needs along the way.

Parents' needs may be organized according to personal and spiritual needs, family needs, and special needs. As you read the following lists of needs, evaluate how well each need is being met in your life. Circle a number on the scale for each need.

	This is a strong need in my life.		I am already doing well in this area.		
Personal spiritual needs					
1. Parents need to recognize the Bible as their trustworthy guide for spiritual growth.	1	2	3	4	5
2. Parents need to develop skills in Bible study.	1	2	3	4	5
3. Parents need the supportive fellowship of the church.	1	2	3	4	5
4. Parents need to understand religious issues in parenting.	1	2	3	4	5
5. Parents need to be able to interpret and apply the Bible in practical and relevant ways.	1	2	3	4	5
6. Parents need to further develop Christian values out of which to parent.	1	2	3	4	5
7. Parents need to understand the strengths and weaknesses in their personalities.	1	2	3	4	5
8. Parents need to develop positive self-images and take care of themselves physically, intellectually, emotionally, and spiritually.	1	2	3	4	5
9. Parents need to understand the stages of parenting through which they move.	1	2	3	4	5

10. Parents need to provide appropriate role models for their children.	1	2	3	4	5
11. Parents need to develop interests of their own that are unrelated to parenting.	1	2	3	4	5
12. Parents need to learn how to let go of their children.	1	2	3	4	5

Family needs
1. Parents need to understand the role of the Christian family.	1	2	3	4	5
2. Parents need to develop an ongoing plan for family worship and Bible study in their homes.	1	2	3	4	5
3. Parents need to work toward enriching their marriages and family life.	1	2	3	4	5
4. Parents need help in guiding the development (moral, spiritual, physical, intellectual, social, emotional) of their children within the family.	1	2	3	4	5
5. Parents need to understand how a Christian family lifestyle relates to a secular society.	1	2	3	4	5

Special needs
1. Parents need to understand any unusual parenting situations in which they find themselves.	1	2	3	4	5
2. Parents need help in relating to the unique challenges and rewards of parenting the physically, intellectually, and/or emotionally handicapped child.	1	2	3	4	5
3. Parents need help in relating to the unique opportunities and hazards of parenting the gifted child.	1	2	3	4	5

Now refer to the two needs you stated at the beginning of this section. Make any changes you wish in your list in light of your evaluation.

Parenting by Grace will help you understand and meet your particular needs as a parent.

Sharing Needs with Other Parents

How can sharing your needs as a parent with other parents be helpful? An old saying suggests that joy is enhanced by sharing while grief is diminished by sharing. Biblical wisdom encourages us to bear one another's burdens. And yet, sharing and caring is risky business. Our ideas and feelings will not always be understood or appreciated. However, we are at a much greater risk if we choose to live in a restrictive cocoon that allows few people to come close or be touched by our life. An openness to life seems essential for the development of healthy relationships.

The value of meeting with other parents facing similar challenges becomes apparent when we find ourselves saying:

"I'm glad I'm not the only mother who looks forward to the baby's afternoon nap."

"Is there ever an end to thumbsucking?"

"How did you and your wife become more consistent about your teenager's homework?"

Throughout this course, specific guidelines will encourage you to actively practice the ideas you have discovered through reading and sharing in a group. Never underestimate the power of God's Spirit to influence your daily living through sharing with fellow Christian parents, studying God's Word, and praying.

State two or three values of parents being able to share common concerns in a supportive group.

* _____

* _____

* _____

Grace—the Foundation of Parenting

Parenting by Grace is built upon the biblical concept of grace. An understanding of grace and its place in the Bible will help to bring into focus its role in the parenting process.

What Is Grace?

Write your own definition of *grace*.

_____

Now find *grace* in a dictionary. Read all the definitions and select the one you think comes closest to the biblical meaning. Write it here.

_____

Grace is the free, unconditional gift of love and mercy from God. Read 2 Timothy 1:9-11. Grace does not depend on anything people may try to do to deserve it. Rather, God has chosen to give His love and mercy to humankind with no strings attached.

Sometimes family members grow up and never know this kind of unconditional love from others in the family. They give and receive love only if certain conditions are met. God's love, however, is freely given regardless of how well people earn or deserve it.

The Biblical Concept of Grace

God's grace is illustrated in the Old Testament by His continuous actions of redemption for His people. Read Isaiah 43:1-15. He reminds them of His watchful care over them and His choice of them as His people. The Israelites experienced God's grace over and over again. Perhaps the most notable time occurred when God delivered them from bondage in Egypt. The memory of deliverance from Egypt was both a humbling and an encouraging experience. The Israelites were reminded that they had been chosen by sheer grace, nothing else.

In Jewish homes of the Old Testament, parenting so that children could come to know God in an intimate relationship was a part of the loyalty and faithfulness God required. This is still true for parents today. Parenting by grace requires that parents relate to their children in all circumstances with unconditional love and mercy, as God the Father does.

The clearest example of God's grace is seen in the coming of Jesus Christ. Through His gift of grace in Christ, God has provided the opportunity for redemption and forgiveness for all persons. Thus, only by accepting God's gift of grace through Jesus Christ can a person enter a right relationship with God (Rom. 3:24).

Such a relationship is necessary for parents to accomplish their God-given task. Parenting by grace allows children to know God by seeing Him in their parents.

An Example of Parenting by Grace

God provided a model of parenting by grace in His choice of Mary and Joseph as the mother and stepfather of Jesus.

Luke gives us the only scene from the childhood of Jesus between His birth and the beginning of His earthly ministry (Luke 2:40-52). When Mary and Joseph found Jesus, who had remained behind at the Temple, they disciplined Him out of love and concern for Him. They recognized His growing independence and spoke to Him out of their anxiety, not out of hostility. Responding to that concern, Jesus went home with them to Nazareth and continued to be obedient to them. Mary and Joseph truly demonstrated parenting by grace as well as learned a great deal about their son.

The parenting style of Mary and Joseph can be inferred from this brief incident: (1) Mary and Joseph took responsibility for guiding their son. (2) They reacted out of respect, not hostility. (3) Jesus accepted parental authority.

Mary and Joseph provided the earthly parenting for God's only Son. Jesus did not spring full grown to earth. Rather, God chose for Him to grow through the normal processes of human development. His earthly parents were entrusted by God with providing love, affirmation, discipline, and guidance He needed to grow as God willed. "And the child continued to grow and become strong, increasing in wisdom; and the grace of God was upon Him" (Luke 2:40, NASB). And the grace of God was upon Him! Who were the earthly ministers of that grace of God being poured upon the boy Jesus? None other than Mary and Joseph!

"And Jesus kept increasing in wisdom and stature, and in favor with God and men" (Luke 2:52, NASB). This one verse spells out the task of Christian parenting. No other verse in the Gospels describes the growth of the child Jesus so completely. The four areas of growth—wisdom (mental and emotional growth), stature (physical growth), in favor with God (spiritual growth) and man (growth in personal relationships)—can be viewed as covering the entire scope of individual growth.

The elements of Christian parenting—love and affirmation, discipline and guidance—serve to help modern children grow in wisdom and stature and in favor with God and significant persons. This is parenting by grace.

Why do you think it is important for children to experience unconditional love from their parents? _____

_____

Why is grace important in the parenting process?

_____

Parenting by Grace Presuppositions

Growing out of the biblical understandings of grace are several presuppositions which undergird parenting by grace.

1. God's grace is freely extended to all persons, including parents.

2. Children are gifts from God, and this is cause for celebration.

3. Biblical principles can be applied to life in our secular society.

4. Christian faith can be communicated to children more effectively as parents clarify what they believe.

5. Parents will grow spiritually as they enhance and improve their parenting skills.

6. God's forgiveness and grace is available to everyone, including parents who are members of nontraditional family units.

7. Parenting skills are passed down from generation to generation.

8. Support can and should be provided at all stages of parents' and children's development.

9. Parents from all ethnic and cultural backgrounds will want to maintain their unique characteristics while fitting into the American culture.

Your Commitment to Parenting by Grace

The effectiveness of this course is dependent on your personal commitment to prepare for, attend, and participate in each session. If you are willing to covenant your best efforts toward the successful completion of the course, complete the following:

> I _____, recognizing the value of Parenting by Grace, do hereby commit to prepare, attend, and participate in each of the sessions. If I am unable to attend a session, I will seek my leader's assistance in make-up work.
>
> _____   _____
> **Signature**   **Date**

Perhaps you feel that this time in your personal, family, or professional life does not allow you to devote the necessary commitment to the successful completion of this course. Your thoughtful, honest approach is appreciated. May we encourage you to prayerfully reconsider the study of Parenting by Grace on another occasion.

Checkpoint

1. Describe briefly in your own words the purpose of Parenting by Grace. _____

_____

_____

2. State two reasons why parenting is significant.

    a. _____

    b. _____

3. List any three trends in parenting.

    a. _____

    b. _____

    c. _____

4. Define grace. _____

_____

5. Explain briefly in your own words the role of grace in parenting. _____

_____

_____

Check your work with the answers in the "Summary."

Reflection and Application

1. Reflect again upon your family and your needs as a parent.

    a. What is your biggest personal and spiritual need? _____

_____

    b. What is the biggest need of your family? _____

_____

    c. What special or unique needs do you have?

2. Turn to the "Purpose of Parenting by Grace" on page 13. Reflect upon the ways the course promises to help you. Jot down what you hope to get out of this course. _____

_____

_____

_____

3. Spend a few minutes reflecting on the following questions. (No written response is necessary.)
   • What are your feelings about this Parenting by Grace course at this time?
   • Why do you think it is so difficult to raise children in today's culture and society?
   • Do your children know that your love for them is unconditional?
   • How has being a parent helped you to grow?
   • What are some ways you experience God's grace in your life?
   • What are some ways your children have seen God's grace at work in your life?
   • What is one significant difference in the family makeup of Mary's and Joseph's home and our homes today?

Summary

1. Parenting by Grace is a ten-lesson course on discipline and spiritual growth. It is designed to help Christian parents understand and use the gift of God's grace in parenting.

2. Parenting is significant because parents are the first major influence in the lives of their children and because of the close emotional ties between parent and child.

3. Trends in parenting include many factors which work against the stability and positive influence of the home. (See page 14 for a listing of some of these trends.)

4. Parents have many needs, including personal and spiritual needs, family needs, and special needs.

5. Grace, the free and unconditional gift of love and mercy from God, is the foundation of effective parenting.

6. It can be inferred that Mary and Joseph parented by grace.

7. A number of presuppositions undergird parenting by grace. (See page 16 for a listing of these.)

8. The effectiveness of this course is dependent on your personal commitment to prepare for, attend, and participate in each session.

Looking Ahead

Lesson 1 is on "Love and Affirmation." The lesson will help you affirm your child(ren). Complete the following activities as you prepare for the lesson.

1. Complete at least one activity for each age group in your family:

• If you are the parent of a preschooler, go for a walk with your child and look for ways God shows us His love in nature. Say short sentence prayers, thanking God for loving us.

• If you are the parent of an elementary-age child, talk with your child about how people can show God's love to others. Be specific and cooperatively plan an activity, such as running an errand, writing a note of appreciation, making a short visit, or offering to complete a household task.

• If you are the parent of a teenager, just for fun, complete the following sentence: "Sometimes, being a parent is like _____." Invite your teenager to complete the sentence: "Sometimes, being a teenager is like _____." Share your responses. Discuss with your teenager where grace (unconditional love) is most needed in your family.

2. Spend a few minutes of quiet reflection about your childhood. Choose one word you would use to best describe your childhood. _____

3. Complete the following chart.

4. Spend a week practicing unconditional love. Put little surprise notes of love and appreciation around the house where family members will find them. At the end of the week, talk about how nice it was to find love notes in surprising places. Relate this to how God freely sends His love to people.

A Comparison of My Childhood with the Childhood of My Children

	My Childhood	My Children's Childhood
Similarities		
Differences		

Unit One

Grace: God's Gift to Parents and Children

Lesson 1
Love and Affirmation

Looking Back

Overview

Learning Goals

Love and Affirmation Defined

Biblical Images of Love and Affirmation

Ways to Show Love and Affirmation

Principles of Love and Affirmation

Checkpoint

Reflection and Application

Summary

Looking Ahead

Looking Back
The introductory lesson focused on two main points: (1) the introduction of Parenting by Grace as a concept and as a course and (2) the importance of your commitment to complete the course.

The lesson emphasized the significance of parenting, some current trends in parenting, the needs of parents, and the value of parents sharing with other parents.

The purpose of Parenting by Grace was presented, along with an overview of the ten lessons in the course. You were then challenged to make a commitment to complete the entire course. Obviously you accepted the challenge—you're back! You have made a worthy commitment.

You prepared for lesson 1 by completing a variety of activities related to love and affirmation. Turn back to page 18 and review these activities. Spend a few minutes reflecting on your involvement in the activities. What were the results of your practicing unconditional love in your family relationships this week?

Overview
This lesson deals with two basics to successful parenting: love and affirmation. These two concepts are defined and then examined in light of Scripture. Three practical ways are suggested by which parents can show love and affirmation for their children, and seven basic principles of love and affirmation are explained.

Learning Goals
After completing this lesson, you should have a better understanding of the importance and use of love and affirmation in the parenting process. You will be able to:
• define love and affirmation as related to parenting,
• summarize in your own words what the Bible teaches about love and affirmation as related to parenting,
• state three ways parents can show love and affirmation for their children,
• state at least four principles of love and affirmation that apply to parenting, and
• affirm your child(ren) on a regular basis.

Love and Affirmation Defined
As we begin the study, write your definition of *love*.

Love is _____
Now find *love* in a dictionary. Select what you think is

the best definition and write it here. _____

_____

Write your definition of *affirmation*.

Affirmation is_____

Now find *affirmation* in the dictionary. Select the best definition and write it below.

_____

_____

To define love is to capture the essence of parenting by grace. Grace is the free unconditional gift of love and mercy by God. God is love. Even as He loves us, we are charged to love and affirm our children. An affirmative response says yes. Loving parents are saying yes to children's need to be honored and cherished, to be affirmed. Affirmation may be defined as validation or confirmation. Children need parents to validate their worth, to confirm their unique and precious value in the sight of God.

Underline the definitions of *love* and *affirmation* in the paragraph above. How do these definitions compare with your own and with the ones given by the dictionary? How are love and affirmation related? (No written response is necessary.)

Select three synonyms for love related to parenting and three for affirmation.

Love _____ _____ _____

Affirmation _____ _____ _____

Biblical Images of Love and Affirmation

Biblical materials that describe God as a God of love and examples of love and affirmation of Christ are essential to our understanding of parenting by grace. God is often called Father in the Scriptures. God the Father is in reality the model parent. In this role the Creator can be seen as the loving, responsible Father who is the source of life.

What image does the word *father* bring to your mind?

_____

_____

To many people, the pictures of God as a Father bring to mind warm, loving images of a tender, intimate relationship with their earthly parents. However, to others, because of poor relationships with their earthly parents, the image of God as a father is frightening or hateful.

God's behavior is determined by His attitude of grace—that unconditional gift of mercy and love—and not by people's attitudes and actions toward Him. As Heavenly Father, God's authority is grounded more in His sacrificial love than in His wrath and revenge. He really is a God of love.

In relating to Israel and to people today, God the "Heavenly Parent" is primarily motivated by love. He acts the way He does because of who He is, not because of what people do. He calls Christian parents today to parent out of the Christian attitude of love. Paul said it well in his letter to the Ephesians: "Therefore be imitators of God, as beloved children; and walk in love, just as Christ also loved you, and gave Himself up for us" (Eph. 5:1-2, NASB).

What are some of the implications the concept of God as Father holds for parenting? Write at least two implications. _____

_____

God knows that only He is God, and we are not. But He expects earthly parents to express love and compassion toward their children.

A theme running through the New Testament is that all relationships should be clothed in love. John felt this strongly and wrote about it in his first letter: "Beloved, let us love one another: for love is of God; and every one that loveth is born of God, and knoweth God. He that loveth not knoweth not God; for God is love" (1 John 4:7-8).

Only those who know the love of God through His Son, Jesus Christ, have a foundation for parenting by grace. When parents know God's love and affirmation through firsthand experience, they can love and affirm their children in turn. Then they can lead their children to develop relationships of mutual love and submission.

What are two ways you have experienced God's love and affirmation in your own life?_____

_____

Ways to Show Love and Affirmation

One of the most touching pictures of love and affirmation for children is given in Mark's Gospel. When people were trying to bring their children to Jesus, some of the disciples scolded them, and Jesus reacted sharply. "Let the children come to me, and do not stop them, because the Kingdom of God belongs to such as these" (Mark 10:14, GNB).

"Let the children come to me"—what a beautiful expression of love and affirmation! There are several things parents today can learn from this. Three ways to show love and affirmation follow:

1. One of the best ways parents can show love and affirmation for their children is through accessibility. Open arms, open hearts, and open ears say "I love you" to children with signals that are loud and clear. If it was important for God's Son to take time to be with children, how much more important it is to make time to be with those children God has entrusted to us!

In what ways are you accessible to your children?

_____

_____

2. Another way parents may show love and affirmation is by being willing to learn from their children. Isaiah spoke of a child leading the people (Isa. 9:6-7).

What is one thing you have learned from your

children? _____

3. A third way to show love and affirmation is through the biblical example of blessing. In biblical times, the practice of blessing came in parents' passing on leadership and property. This showed the child that the parents had great expectations for the child's future.

Turn in your Bible to Genesis 48 and read the story of Jacob blessing his two grandsons, the sons of Joseph.

What significance do you think this blessing from their 147-year-old grandfather held for Ephraim and Manasseh? _____

How can we apply the biblical idea of blessing as parents today? _____

Children's self-esteem can be influenced greatly when they feel their parents believe in them and have hope for their future. Tell your children they are loved and respected just for being who they are. Give children gifts that have deep personal or family meaning behind them.

How do you communicate to your children that you believe in them and have hope for their future?

What was the best gift you ever received from your parents? _____

Complete the statement: "If I could give my child any gift I choose, I would give the gift of _____

Write three ways parents can show love and affirmation for their children. Refer to the text as needed.

a. _____

b. _____

c. _____

Principles of Love and Affirmation

1. *"Thou shalt love the Lord thy God with all thy heart, and with all thy soul, and with all thy strength, and with all thy mind"* (Luke 10:27). How appropriate that lesson 1 in Parenting by Grace focuses on love and affirmation. The first principle in the first lesson is to love the Lord thy God.

To love and give Him first place in your affections is to establish a proper perspective in your family life. When parents are in right relationship with God, their behavior will be guided by the Holy Spirit (Gal. 5:16). Such parents' lives—and their relationship with their children— will demonstrate the fruit of the Spirit: love, joy, peace, patience, kindness, goodness, faithfulness, gentleness, and self-control (Gal. 5:22-23, NASB).

This number one principle of love and affirmation requires that parents continue to grow in their own understanding of God. The better we understand God's

loving spirit as the model parent, the more accurately we can portray His love to our children.

2. *"Thou shalt love the Lord thy God . . . and thy neighbor . . ."* (Luke 10:27). Who are your neighbors? Who are the significant others in your life? At first glance, loving parents, spouse, and children appears to come easily and naturally in many families. Beyond this relatively small circle of close, familiar, loving associates, the neighbors may become more difficult to love.

Why should we be concerned about loving our neighbors (other than spouses and children) in a parenting course? In lesson 3 we will recognize the responsibility of parents to encourage children's spiritual development. One major aspect of spiritual development is growing in our understanding and love for others.

3. *"Thou shalt love the Lord thy God . . . and thy neighbour as thyself"* (Luke 10:27). Love yourself? Yes. We have been made in the image or likeness of God. If we assume we are of little value, it is to say that God didn't know what He was doing when He made us. God loves us; therefore we are of great value and infinite worth to God.

The Bible infers that a person must love himself before he can love others. Some adults have the advantage of having developed a healthy self-concept prior to becoming parents. If you felt loved and appreciated as a child with special gifts as well as unique opportunities for service, you probably developed a positive self-concept.

Why do you think some persons have a poor self-concept? _____

What if you were not so fortunate? What if you have negative feelings about yourself? How do you begin to build your self-esteem? A reverent view of your value from God's perspective is a beginning place.

Read Psalm 8:1-9, Psalm 139:1-6, 13-18, and Matthew 6:25-34. Then answer these questions:

What is the place of persons in God's creation?

_____

What is the value of a person in God's sight?

_____

What do these passages teach concerning the need for a healthy self-concept? _____

_____

Once you are convicted of your singular value in God's sight, you are encouraged to live out God's plan for your life. God's plan for families challenges parents to take care of themselves physically, intellectually, emotionally, and spiritually. Children's needs are best met by adults whose needs are met.

4. *Unconditionally love your children.* Grace is the free, unconditional gift of love and mercy from God (2 Tim. 1:9). It does not depend on anything people may try to do to deserve it. Rather, God has chosen to give His love and mercy with no strings attached; the only condition to be met is acceptance of His love in Jesus Christ. Parenting by God's grace requires that parents relate to their children in all circumstances with unconditional love and mercy, as God the Father does.

Unconditional love does not mean your child is free to do anything she pleases. In fact, because you do love your child, you identify certain limits, standards of behavior, and reasonable expectations of her.

5. *Love your child and attack the problem(s) rather than attacking the child with problem(s).* No family's life together is smooth sailing all the time. When a problem occurs, continue to love your child and keep in mind that you can respond with your actions, words, and indirect guidance.

The younger the child, the more appropriate some types of physical guidance are likely to be. The older the child, the more appropriate verbal guidance becomes. Indirectly, we guide children with our attitudes, expectations, and the environment provided for children of various ages.

What is an example of physical guidance?

_____

What is an example of verbal guidance?

_____

What is an example of indirect guidance?

_____

6. *Love and affirm your child by respecting his unique personality and developmental characteristics.* Respect may be defined as high or special regard. To respect your child is to consider him of great value, deserving your esteem.

To respect and honor the unique personality of your child implies that you will minimize comparison or competition with other children. Instead of constantly comparing his accomplishment with siblings or friends, you compare his progress with his own previous accomplishments.

An unconditional, loving acceptance of your preschooler means that you celebrate his remembering to stay at the table until he finishes his meal. You do not suggest that his older sister accomplished this feat at a much earlier age.

When your elementary-age child begins his homework without a parental reminder, you affirm her behavior. You do not emphasize that the child next door has been practicing this procedure for several months.

As your teenager folds clean laundry and starts din-

ner prior to your arrival, you celebrate her thoughtfulness and initiative. You do not describe how your colleague's teenager has been assuming complete responsibility for planning and preparing the evening meals during the past summer.

Avoiding constant comparison and competition between children does not mean they are unaware of other children's accomplishments. Parents need to help children understand themselves and their peers. Understanding self and others doesn't necessarily mean approval or disapproval of specific behaviors or attitudes. Unconditional acceptance of self and others does mean the acknowledgment of individual strengths and weaknesses.

Love and affirm your child at each developmental level. Sometimes we, as parents, seem to want to push or pull the child to the next higher level. Perhaps we say: "You're too old to be acting that way. You should know better than to hit your little brother." Keep in mind that growing up is often an uneven staircase. Your child may appear to move along in a steady fashion for a while. At other times, he seems to take a tumble or take one step up and two steps down. Your unconditional acceptance of him, even as you redirect his behavior, is essential for the full development of his potential.

Sometimes we seem to want to hold our children at a more immature level. We find ourselves saying: "You're not old enough to do that. When you're a little older you can . . ." Reasonable expectations for your child at each developmental level will help you say, "You're exactly the right age to: paint at an easel, spend the night with grandmother, bake cookies by yourself, learn to drive a car." Celebrate regularly the "just right age" for learning and growing toward maturity.

Write a summary description of your child(ren). If you have two or more children, note similarities and differences in them. Use separate sheets of paper for your work.

How can you become more aware of the unique personality and developmental characteristics of your

child(ren)? _____

_____

What is one practical action you can take to show more respect for the uniqueness of your child(ren)?

_____

7. *Practice love and affirmation.* It is important that parents have the ability to affirm their children—that is, being able to express their pleasure and pride in their children to the children themselves. This skill may not be as easy to practice as it sounds. Sometimes we're hesitant or reluctant to express the positive feelings we have for our children.

You may want to begin by expressing your positive feelings in written form.

Write your child(ren) a love letter. Remember the love letters you wrote to your spouse before or right after you were married? They were probably full of love, acceptance, encouragement, and hope. Write a letter like that to your child(ren). Tell them about your unconditional love for them. State positively that you accept who they are and what they like and dislike. Give your encouragement to the development of their gifts and talents. Affirm their unique personalities and developmental characteristics. Tell them of your hopes and dreams for their future. You may choose whether to write one letter to all of your children together or an individual letter to each child. If your child is very young, write the letter and save it for a special occasion when she is older.

Stop and write the letter now.

In addition to a love letter, how can you express your love and affirmation for your child? An unexpected note in a child's coat pocket, lunch box, typewriter, or Bible can reinforce your positive supportive attitude toward your child's development.

To help you hone your skill of affirmation, practice it on your spouse, friends, neighbors, or colleagues. Muriel F. Blackwell, a Christian educator, describes the need for a "Say So Journey." She suggests that as you become aware of positive feelings toward others, you need to take a "Say So Journey." That is, you need to go to those persons and let them know of your feelings of admiration, appreciation, love, and gratitude. If you care about others, you need to affirm them by saying so.

Some persons may initially have difficulty accepting your expressions of affirmation. Too many persons have grown up in families that seldom express their deepest emotions in a verbal way. Yes, actions speak louder than words. However, sometimes a word of encouragement, appreciation, and thanksgiving can be affirming and uplifting.

What is one "Say So Journey" you can take with your child(ren)? _____

_____

Honesty is an integral part of a healthy relationship with your child. Honesty dictates acknowledgment of all feelings. If you are disappointed or annoyed or aware of wrongdoing, perhaps a "Say So Journey" is the beginning of resolution.

As we share our own negative feelings, children sense that all feelings are legitimate. How to share negative feelings in a constructive manner is an invalu-

able lesson for children to learn.

The use of "I" messages may be less threatening than "you" messages. We might say: "I'm tired and need your help in getting ready for bed," rather than, "You are always playing instead of putting away your toys before bedtime." Try saying, "I'm disappointed in your math grade. How can I help you with long-division problems?" rather than, "You obviously aren't paying attention to your teacher." To our teenager we might say, "I was so very worried about your being late; I was afraid you might have had an accident," rather than, "Can't you tell time? You scared me to death when you were late coming home."

Why are "I" messages less threatening than "you"

messages? _____

What did you notice about the "I" messages? They shared negative feelings in an open, honest, "let's talk about it" approach.

What did you notice about the "you" messages? They were accusatory in nature: accusing the child before she had an opportunity to understand our feelings and search for a cooperative approach to problem solving.

Turn back and underline each of the seven principles of love and affirmation.

Write the seven principles on a separate sheet of paper. Refer to the text as needed.

Checkpoint

Let's stop and review the key points and concepts in this lesson. Complete the following exercises.

1. Define *love* as related to parenting.

_____

2. Define *affirmation* as related to parenting.

_____

3. Summarize briefly in your own words what the Bible teaches about love and affirmation as related to parenting.

_____

_____

_____

4. State three ways parents can show love and affirmation for their children.

a. _____

b. _____

c. _____

5. State at least four principles of love and affirmation that apply to parenting.

a. _____

b. _____

c. _____

d. _____

Check your work with the answers given in the "Summary."

Reflection and Application

1. What are some things that make it easy for you to show God's kind of love to your child(ren)? _____

_____

2. What are some things that make it difficult for you to show God's kind of love to your child(ren)? _____

_____

3. What words do you think your child would use in describing his relationship with you? _____

_____

4. It is easy for me to give my child affirmation when she . . . (give several examples)

_____

_____

5. It is difficult for me to give my child affirmation when he . . . (give several examples)

_____

_____

6. Evaluate yourself regarding the priorities of your life. Number the following items from 1 to 9 in their relative value in your priorities. Assign 1 to the highest priority, 2 to the second highest priority, etc. Then rank the items as you think your child would perceive your priorities.

How I rank the priorities in my life	Priority	How I think my child would perceive my priorities
	work	
	sleep	
	house	
	God	
	church	
	spouse	
	child	
	hobby/ recreation	
	other	

Is your ranking consistent with the way you spend your time and money and with the choices you make?

Do you think your child's perception of your priorities would differ from your own ranking? If so, why?

7. Write a one-sentence definition of *unconditional love* using one syllable words. _____

_____

8. What is the tension between unconditional love and the setting of limitations and restrictions? _____

_____

9. Share with your child the letter you wrote. How do you think your child felt about receiving the letter? Did he say anything to you about this letter?

10. Check yourself this week to see how many "I" messages and "you" messages you give your child. Use the chart to record the number.

Day	Number of "I" messages I give my child(ren)	Number of "you" messages I give my child(ren)
Sunday		
Monday		
Tuesday		
Wednesday		
Thursday		
Friday		
Saturday		

11. Look for one behavior or action by your child this week over which you can express affirmation and celebration. Record the behavior below and what you did to affirm and celebrate.

Action	Affirmation and Celebration

Summary

1. Love is Godlike; it is God's grace in action. Love in parenting is honoring, cherishing, and affirming your child.

2. Affirmation is validation or confirmation of a child's worth and value.

3. The Bible teaches that God is our Heavenly Father and loves us with an unconditional and sacrificial love. He expects us to express this kind of love and affirmation to our children.

4. Three ways we can show love and affirmation for our children.
- Through our accessibility
- By being willing to learn from our children
- Through the biblical example of blessing

5. Seven principles of love and affirmation that apply to parenting:
- Give God first place in your life.
- Love others (children, spouse, neighbors).
- Have a healthy self-concept.
- Unconditionally love your children.
- Love your child and attack the problem(s).
- Love and affirm your child by respecting her uniqueness.
- Practice love and affirmation.

Looking Ahead

Lesson 2 deals with discipline and guidance. Your study will center around nine basic principles of discipline and guidance that apply to parenting.

In addition to reading lesson 2, complete the following activities.

1. We should strive to discipline our children in the same way God disciplines. On the left side of the chart below is a list of words that describe God's discipline toward us, His children. On the right side is space for you to give a specific example of how you can show that same characteristic in the relationship you have with your children. The first response is completed as an example.

Characteristic of God	How Can I Apply This Characteristic?
patient	Instead of losing my temper when my child says no, I'll deal with him quietly.
forgiving	
consistent	
compassionate	
guiding	
gracious	
encouraging	

2. Carefully consider and write down the most difficult problem you face with discipline?

_____

_____

3. How were you most often punished as a child?

_____

What seem to be the long-term effects of that type of punishment in your life? _____

_____

Lesson 2
Discipline and Guidance

Looking Back

In lesson 1 the central theme of love and affirmation was highlighted. Emphasis was placed on love and affirmation as the two basics to successful parenting. These two concepts were defined and examined in light of Scripture. Then three practical ways were suggested by which you can show love and affirmation for your children, and seven basic principles of love and affirmation were explained. The main purpose of the chapter was to help you affirm your children on a regular basis.

You prepared for lesson 2 by completing several activities related to discipline and guidance. Turn back to page 26 and review these activities. Spend a few minutes reflecting on what you did. Were you able to apply the characteristics of God as you related to your child(ren) through the week? Which one did you practice least?

Overview

This lesson deals with discipline and guidance. Discipline is defined and then examined in light of Scripture. Nine practical principles of discipline and guidance are explained, and the difference is pointed out between discipline and punishment.

Learning Goals

After completing this lesson, you should have a better understanding of the nature and use of discipline and guidance in parenting. You will be able to:

- define *discipline* as related to parenting,
- summarize in your own words what the Bible teaches about discipline and guidance as related to parenting,
- state at least four principles of discipline and guidance that apply to parenting,
- explain the difference between discipline and punishment,
- identify one behavioral problem or pattern with your child that requires discipline, and
- outline plans for disciplining your child in response to the behavioral problem identified.

Discipline Defined

Write one word that comes to your mind when you think

of discipline._____

Ask each of your children who are old enough to share with you the first word that he thinks of upon hear-

ing the word *discipline*. Write the words here: _____

_____

Find *discipline* in a dictionary. Select what you think is

the best definition and write it here._____

_____

For many parents, discipline means a stern reprimand, the removal of privileges, or spanking. In parenting by grace, though, discipline means much more. The word *discipline* comes from a Latin word which means "to teach." Discipline means guidance or teaching. The goal of discipline is to guide our children to become self-controlled and self-directed so they can live under the Lordship of Christ. When mothers and fathers are parenting by grace, discipline works itself out of a job. The ultimate goal is self-discipline.

Underline the definition of *discipline* in the paragraph above. How does this definition compare with or relate to the words thought of by you and your children? How does the definition compare with one given by the dictionary? (No written response is necessary.)

There are two major aspects of self-discipline. The first is developing personal habits such as diet and personal hygiene, avoiding drugs (except as prescribed by a physician) and alcohol, relating to others responsibly in expressing sexuality, and developing physical and spiritual fitness. This type of discipline, from the Christian perspective, is expressed in Romans 12:1. "Offer your bodies as living sacrifices, holy and pleasing to God—which is your spiritual worship" (NIV). Second, we want our children to become self-disciplined in making responsible decisions and carrying them through. Discipline by grace, then, involves far more than punishing children for misbehavior.

Select three synonyms for *discipline* and write them below:

_____

_____

_____

Now write your own definition of *discipline* as related

to parenting. _____

The Bible Speaks to Discipline and Guidance

Read each of the following statements. If you agree with the statement, write *A* in the blank. If you disagree with the statement, write *D*. The statements are not necessarily true or false, but you should be able to state whether you agree or disagree with them.

_____ 1. The Bible says very little, either by precept or example, about the discipline of children.

_____ 2. Discipline of children in the Old Testament refers to corporal punishment.

_____ 3. Discipline in the Bible as a whole implies instruction and guidance.

_____ 4. Discipline and love are closely related in the Bible.

Here is how I responded to the statements. Number 1—disagree. I think the Bible says a great deal about the discipline of children. Number 2 is tricky. Whereas the discipline of children in the Old Testament does refer at times to corporal punishment, the main emphasis is instruction and guidance. Number 3—agree. Number 4—agree.

The Bible speaks directly to parents concerning discipline and guidance. The ancient Israelites did not believe in "education without tears." From the frequent references to the rod in the Old Testament and because of the various meanings of rod, one can be fairly certain that the ancient Israelites used corporal punishment as one method of discipline (see Prov. 10:13; 13:24; 22:15; 23:13; 29:15; 2 Sam. 7:14-15). The purpose of corporal punishment was to bring about children's reform. It was not a means by which parents were to vent their wrath upon their children.

The word chasten means to correct and improve by means of punishment. Wise parents realize that chastening or punishment should be corrective, not destructive (see Heb. 12:3-11; Prov. 13:24; 2 Sam. 7:14-15; Rev. 3:19).

On the other hand, many uses of discipline in the Old Testament implied simple instruction and correction. The father was held responsible for the religious education of his son and for teaching the traditions of the chosen people (see Deut. 6:6-9).

Parental love needs to include discipline, supervision, nurture, and reproof. Love and discipline are closely related. In fact, to fail to discipline proves a lack of parental love (Prov. 13:24).

The writer of Proverbs has given parents the beautiful promise, "Train up a child in the way he should go, even when he is old he will not depart from it" (Prov. 22:6, NASB). A key phrase in this verse is "in the way he should go." This means literally "according to his way," that is. In keeping with the child's unique personality, temperament, and aptitude. Every child deserves the love of parents that sees him as a special gift from God. Proverbs 22:6 emphasizes that carefully planned and insightful training of children is important and has long-range consequences.

Read Proverbs 22:6 from several translations. Then write your own paraphrase of the verse.

_____

_____

_____

Old Testament discipline must be refined with New Testament grace. This will add more elements of teaching and guidance. When the New Testament view of grace is added to an understanding of Old Testament discipline, parents have more options of instruction, teaching, and guidance. The result is love and affirmation, discipline and guidance. Think of a symbol that for you best represents the biblical teachings concerning discipline. Draw a sketch of the symbol in the margin of this paper. (You will be asked to share it in the group session.)

Summarize briefly what the Bible teaches concerning discipline and guidance.

_____

_____

_____

Principles of Discipline and Guidance

Practical implications of a biblical understanding of discipline and guidance suggest certain basic principles. Principles are generally applicable to children of various developmental levels in a variety of circumstances. As you study the following principles, think of ways you can apply and make use of each principle with your own children.

1. *Try to understand children's development in general and your child's development in particular.*

Understanding children's behavior may be the primary prerequisite for appropriate discipline to occur. In lesson 3 more attention will be given to this important aspect of parenting by grace.

What is one action you can take to understand better your child's behavior and development?

_____

2. *Be a good listener.*

A key element for understanding and disciplining your child appropriately is listening. From the earliest days of your baby's life, she attempts to communicate needs. Sensitive listening at each age of development is the starting point for meeting needs.

If your child has learned to trust you to listen and attempt to meet his needs, respect his expression of feelings, and allow him to initiate appropriate plans and ideas, then you are being a good listener.

Identify one problem you have in listening to your child. _____

3. *Be a good observer.*

One goal of disciplining your child may be to influence or change the child's behavior. If we are interested in shaping behavior, we must first study or observe the behavior.

Does your baby's behavior become more restless in the late afternoon or early evening? Is this when you are less fresh and need a helping hand from a spouse, an older child, or a neighbor? Does your preschooler's thumbsucking occur primarily when he is sleepy or disinterested with the available activities? Does your elementary-age children's table manners seem to go awry when guests come for dinner? Does your behavior need to be more consistent? Would encouraging good manners on a regular basis lay the framework for special occasions? Does your teenager's poor study habits suggest a pattern of behavior that will become increasingly less effective in completing homework? Would cooperation with your teen's teachers or counselor be a first step toward more effective study habits?

How does this principle relate to principle number 1?

_____

4. *Speak kindly, quietly, and yet firmly.*

"Be ye kind" (Eph. 4:32) is often taught to children. As parents we need to relearn the value of a kind, considerate approach. Speaking quietly to children has a biblical foundation. According to Proverbs 15:1, a soft answer turns away wrath.

A pattern of unkind, critical, or oppressive remarks may lead to unhappy, discouraged children. Some children withdraw into quiet resignation. They begin to believe the caustic, harsh words directed toward them. Convinced that they are unworthy, they may be quietly obedient to demanding parents. Their emotional development is warped, and their potential to lead healthy, happy, contributing Christian lives is thwarted.

Other children respond to aggressive, hostile words by becoming aggressive and hostile themselves. As they "fight back," a self-defeating cycle of more angry words and behavior is set in motion. The joy and happiness of the parent-child relationship is being snuffed out on a regular basis.

Speaking quietly to your preschooler may mean physically moving closer to her. Go across the room, stoop, bend, or sit so that you look into your child's face. Speaking quietly to your elementary-age child may mean remaining calm when things have gotten out of hand. Children need to be able to count on adults staying in control. Speaking quietly to your teenager may mean arranging special opportunities for honest, open communication. Share a burger or a pizza and talk about how things are going.

Does speaking softly mean you are a "softie" or a "pushover"? The consistency of your expectations coupled with a quiet and yet firm approach is an effective aspect of parenting by grace.

When and how did you last violate this principle?

_____

_____

5. *Speak on the child's level.*

Obviously this can mean on the child's eye level and in close physical proximity as discussed previously. In addition, speaking on the child's level can be interpreted as taking into account the child's level of development.

Giving your child too many directives at one time is sure to lead to confusion or distraction. In some instances, you are more helpful to your child if you give specific examples as you guide his behavior. Try hard to neither talk down nor expect too much too soon when communicating with your child.

Why is it difficult for parents to speak on the child's

level?_____

6. *Child-proof the environment.*

Does your home have that lived-in look? Hopefully an objective observer would recognize that a preschooler or an elementary-age child or teenager lives in your home. The need for a space of one's own seems to be an inborn "nesting" phenomenon.

Child proofing the environment allows you to focus on a positive interacting with your children. Less time and attention is spent protecting valuable, breakable items. More time is spent developing an invaluable and unbreakable bond with your child.

What is one action you can take to child proof your

home more effectively?_____

7. *Identify appropriate limits.*

This may be the most often quoted principle of discipline. Is it really that important? The necessity of limits becomes apparent in almost every aspect of life. When presented with a new situation, the search for limits begins. What may I do? What must I avoid? What are the rules of the game?

Sometimes we assume children would be perfectly happy if they were perfectly free. If the concept of permissiveness is carried too far, it is almost saying to the child, "You are permitted to do whatever you want because I don't care." But when we care, we care enough to identify appropriate limits.

Limits reassure children that parents' love and concern can be depended upon to guide and restrict their behavior. A complete sense of freedom can be frightening, almost overwhelming. Children are more comfortable with a degree of freedom within appropriate limits.

The possibility of revising and extending limits is a reoccurring challenge for parents. You ask yourself or your spouse, "Is she ready to spend the weekend with her grandmother? Is he ready for swimming lessons this summer? Is she ready to start kindergarten? Is he ready to go to church camp? Is she ready to begin dating?"

Children sometimes tell you when they are ready for new and revised limits. Pushing against and testing old limits may suggest parents should reconsider the rules or boundaries. Maybe he is old enough to stay by himself for an hour or so without a baby-sitter. Think of the

new limits and guidelines for which the child must assume responsibility when staying by himself for the first few times. Imagine his feelings of accomplishment and independence when he successfully manages this time alone.

On occasion, children push against and test limits when they really want you to remain firm. You may consistently remind your preschooler that bedtime comes at a regular time after certain routine activities. You may quietly and firmly insist that your elementary-age children discuss ways of sharing a new game rather than physically struggling over the pieces of the game. You remain true to the established curfew on a school night even though your teenager may momentarily push for a later time to come home. Your firmness in these situations reassures children that your care and concern is regularly expressed in everyday limits.

Identify two specific areas where you have set limits for your children and state those limits.

AREA	LIMITS I HAVE SET

8. *Consistently maintain necessary limits.*

The value of consistency in parenting can be seen most clearly in contrast to inconsistency.

Inconsistency is basically unfair. To be allowed to race through the living room on one occasion and be severely reprimanded on another occasion for the same behavior is confusing to the preschooler. Elementary-age children will be the first to cry, "It's not fair," if one sibling stays up later than his usual bedtime. Teenagers become increasingly sensitive to inconsistency in our lives as parents. If we have taught the lesson of the "Good Samaritan," our children have every right to look for the lesson to be lived out in our daily lives.

A little advanced notice helps children prepare for changes or inconsistencies in their lives. You might say, "When Grandmother comes to visit us, she will need to stay in your bedroom. She cannot climb the stairs as easily as you can. You may take some of your clothes and games from your room to the upstairs guest bedroom where you will sleep."

Apparent inconsistencies may occur because of differences in approaches of parenting. Explanations may help children understand. You might say, "Your father needs us to be extra quiet when he is working on his papers." You may be able to work with children underfoot. Your spouse may need periods of quiet. Try to honor the unique, positive aspects of each parent, grandparent, and teacher in your child's life. Each of you contributes to his preparation for a world of unique persons.

What is one problem you have in consistently maintaining limits you have set for your children?

9. *Encourage the child's development of freedom within limits.*

Once necessary limits have been established, they should be clearly defined and consistently maintained. In fact, children may need to do some isometric exercises. Isometric exercises involve pushing against something that does not give in with pressure.

Children are reassured to know that some guidelines, limits, and restrictions are going to remain in place regardless of the circumstances or situations. Within these basic limits, there is plenty of room for children to develop a healthy sense of freedom and autonomy.

As Americans we pride ourselves on being an autonomous people. We value the opportunity for self-governance and independence. When and how is this aspect of children's development encouraged?

One of the best ways to reinforce preschoolers' feelings of independence is to provide opportunities for them to make choices. Keeping in mind that the choices should be within limits, you might say: "It is cold this morning, so you must wear warm slacks. You may choose to wear the red or yellow sweatshirt."

If you ask, "What do you want for breakfast?" you have failed to indicate any limits. It is preferable to identify the choices: "You may choose toast or muffins to eat with your cereal."

Give a child choices only when you are prepared to accept his decision. Have you ever asked your child, "Are you ready to go to bed?" That suggests the child has a choice. In situations where there is no choice, give children a bit of advanced notice. You might say, "After we read one more story, you must get into bed."

Studies indicate that elementary-age children either feel that "I can make things happen" or "Things happen to me." Obviously this basic difference in attitude reflects the degree of autonomy or independence they feel in their young lives.

Children who have developed good self-control feel they exercise a healthy degree of control over their lives. Children who are externally controlled or influenced feel they are victims of fate. External forces, over which they exercise little control, govern their lives.

The widespread and long-term consequences of a healthy sense of autonomy are apparent during the teen years. An adolescent with good self-control is less vulnerable to external (peer) pressure. She feels more comfortable saying no and sticking by her decision.

What is one specific thing you do to encourage your child's development of freedom within limits?

_____

Turn back and underline each of the nine principles of discipline and grace.

See how many of the principles you can list without referring to any notes. Any order is acceptable. They can be in your own words.

1. _____
2. _____
3. _____
4. _____
5. _____
6. _____
7. _____
8. _____
9. _____

Difference Between Discipline and Punishment

The difference between discipline and punishment relates directly to the difference between God's grace and God's laws. In Jesus Christ we no longer live under the law (see Gal. 5:1-6). God no longer deals with us in punishment—giving us what we deserve—but with His grace. God disciplines us because He loves us and wants the best for us. He helps us grow up in faith. "God disciplines us for our good, that we may share in his holiness" (Heb. 12:10).

When children act in unacceptable ways, under the law we punish them—they get what they deserve. And that's where it ends. In contrast, discipline by grace responds to children's misbehavior by examining their attitudes and motives. The emphasis in grace is on the growth of the child, not the child's misdeeds. Under a system of law and punishment, children obey out of fear of what will happen if they misbehave. Under discipline by grace, children obey out of love and respect for their parents and a desire to please them (see Heb. 12:9).

Discipline by grace does not mean that our children do not receive punishment. In fact the parent who disciplines by grace and the parent who punishes may outwardly respond to a child's misbehavior in similar ways. But the motivation and attitude behind the response and the follow-up is different. According to Bruce Narramore:

A child may be sent to his room for example, for either corrective discipline or punishment. If a child misbehaves and is sent to his room in anger, he is being punished. The attitude is anger, the purpose is retribution, and the focus is past action. But if a child misbehaves and is calmly and lovingly sent to his room in order to promote his understanding and growth, there is constructive discipline. Discipline carried out from a perspective of grace, lovingly establishes limits and corrects in an authoritative, but not an authoritarian, manner.[1]

As a result of discipline, individuals are more likely to become self-disciplined, self-motivated, self-directed, self-fulfilled. Too often punishment leads individuals to remain dependent upon others to direct their lives. They do what is right in order to receive a reward, and they are motivated to avoid the wrong behavior only to avoid punishment.

Complete the chart by writing one word in each box. Refer to the preceding paragraphs to find the words.

A Contrast Between Punishment and Discipline

	Punishment	Discipline
1. The emphasis is on . . .		
2. The child obeys out of . . .		
3. The attitude of the parent is often that of . . .		
4. The purpose is . . .		
5. The result is . . .		

Explain in your own words the difference between discipline and punishment. _____

_____

Here are the words I chose in contrasting punishment and discipline in the chart above: 1. misdeeds—growth; 2. fear—love; 3. anger—love; 4. retribution—growth; 5. dependency—self-discipline. Of course your words need not be identical to mine.

Checkpoint

It's time to review the key points in this lesson. Complete the following exercise.

1. Define *discipline* as related to parenting.

_____

_____

2. Summarize briefly in your own words what the Bible teaches about discipline and guidance as related to parenting. _____

3. State at least four principles of discipline and guidance that apply to parenting.

a. _____

b. _____

c. _____

d. _____

4. Explain the difference between discipline and punishment. _____

_____

Check your work with the answers given in the "Summary."

Reflection and Application

1. Continue your record of the number of "I" messages and "you" messages you give your children this week. Work to decrease the number of "you" messages.

Day	Number of "I" messages I give my child(ren)	Number of "you" messages I give my child(ren)
Sunday		
Monday		
Tuesday		
Wednesday		
Thursday		
Friday		
Saturday		

[1]Bruce Narramore, "Discipline by Grace," *Journal of Psychology and Theology*, I (1979), 263-270.

2. Continue your practice of affirmation and celebration. Look for a behavior or action by each child this week over which you can express affirmation and celebration. Complete the chart.

Child's name	Child's action	Affirmation and celebration

3. Keep a record of your child's behavior for one week. Study again principle number 3 before you do this. Look especially for behavior patterns where discipline and guidance are needed. Use a separate sheet of paper for your notes.

4. Identify one behavioral problem or pattern with your child that requires discipline. Describe the problem. _____

5. Plan how you can discipline your child in response to the behavioral problem or pattern identified. Outline your plans on a separate sheet of paper.

6. List at least one method of discipline and guidance, other than punishment, that a parent could use with each of the following ages of children.

Stages	Method of Discipline and Guidance (other than punishment)	Immediate Results
Preschooler		
Elementary-age		
Teenager		

Try at least one of these methods of discipline and guidance with your child(ren) this week. Note the immediate results and write them on the chart.

Summary

1. Discipline is the teaching and guidance of a child to help him to become self-disciplined.

2. The Bible teaches that parents are responsible for guiding, instructing, and correcting their children. Love is an integral part of discipline. "Teach a child how he should live, and he will remember it all his life" (Prov. 22:6, GNB).

3. Nine principles of discipline and guidance that apply to parenting:
   - Understand your child's development.
   - Be a good listener.
   - Be a good observer.
   - Speak kindly, quietly, and yet firmly.
   - Speak on the child's level.
   - Child-proof the environment.
   - Identify appropriate limits.
   - Consistently maintain necessary limits.
   - Encourage the child's development of freedom within limits.

4. Discipline grows out of love and focuses on growth and self-discipline; punishment grows out of anger and focuses on the misdeeds of the child, retribution, and dependency.

Looking Ahead

Lesson 3 deals with the physical, moral, and spiritual development of children and your responsibility for your children's development.

In addition to reading lesson 3, complete one of the following activities. Use a separate sheet of paper for your notes.

1. A child learns his first lesson about God through his relationship with his parents. Note some specific examples of lessons your child is learning about God from his relationship with you.

2. Observe your child's particular stage of development. Write a brief, concise description of his level of development at this time. Are your expectations for your child's behavior "just right" at this time? Are you expecting too much or too little?

Unit Two

Helping Children Grow According to God's Plan

Lesson 3
Physical, Moral, and Spiritual Development

Looking Back

Lesson 2 emphasized the significance of discipline and guidance in parenting by grace. God disciplines out of love, not from a punitive stance, and so should we as parents. Discipline was defined as guidance and teaching with a strong distinction made between discipline and punishment. Nine practical principles of discipline and guidance were set forth. Turn to the "Summary" of lesson 2 on page 33 and review the nine principles.

You prepared for lesson 3 by completing an activity related to children's physical, moral, and spiritual development. Turn to page 33 and review this activity. Spend a few minutes reflecting on what you did.

Overview

This lesson discusses the physical, moral, and spiritual development of children. Growth, maturation, and learning are defined and then four principles of child development are presented. The developmental stages of children are identified, and parental responsibility for their children's development is pinpointed. The developmental needs of each age group are identified, along with the unique needs of children who find themselves in special circumstances.

Learning Goals

After completing this lesson, you should have a better understanding of the physical, moral, and spiritual development of your children. You will be able to—

• select from a given list of definitions the correct ones for *growth, maturation, and learning;*

• state four principles of child development;

• describe briefly the typical characteristics of the developmental stage of each of your children;

• name three persons a parent must know in order to parent by grace;

• identify from a given list of developmental needs the ones to which you need to give special attention in order to help your children in their development;

• state two specific actions you can take to assist your children in their development.

Growth, Maturation, and Learning Defined

To define children's development is to recognize the challenge and complexity of parenting by grace. Development occurs as the result of the interaction of growth, maturation, and learning.

Select the best definition of each of the following words from your dictionary and write it in the blank.

Growth _____

Maturation _____

Learning _____

Growth is generally used to describe the more obvious, tangible, concrete changes in children's lives. The eight-month-old has grown two new teeth. The elementary-age child is losing and gaining two new teeth. The teenager has grown taller than her mother. Growth may be fairly easy to identify and measure, a quantitative change.

Underline one word in the paragraph above that for you best describes the kind of change caused by growth.

On the other hand, *maturation* is sometimes defined as qualitative changes in the individual. Maturational or qualitative changes may be more subtle and difficult to quantify than changes due to growth. Maturation is less influenced by the environment than is learning.

Underline one word in the paragraph above that for you best describes the kind of change caused by maturation.

Learning can be defined as a change in behavior or attitude. Obviously learning is highly influenced by the environment.

Underline the definition of learning in the above paragraph. I underlined *quantitative* as the kind of change caused by growth and *qualitative* as the kind of change caused by maturation.

Principles of Child Development

The following statements pertain to child development. If the statement is true, write *T* in the blank. If the statement is false, write *F* in the blank.

_____ 1. The *order* of development varies little from one child to another.

_____ 2. The *rate* of development varies greatly from one child to another.

_____ 3. Development proceeds in stages and each stage has characteristic traits.

_____ 4. Development is cumulative.

Development is the result of the interaction of growth, maturation, and learning. All of the statements above are true; in fact, the statements are four important principles of child development. Let's examine the principles individually.

1. *The order of development varies little from one child to another.* Almost all children will sit before they stand and stand before they walk.

2. *The rate of development varies greatly from one child to another.* Within the range of normal develop-

ment, some children will say first words several months earlier or several months later than other children. the rate of development varies even more extensively with special children.

3. *Development proceeds in stages, and each stage has characteristic traits.* Much of this lesson will focus on the needs and characteristics of preschool children, elementary-age children, and teenagers.

4. *Development is cumulative.* One stage builds on the previous stages. A good beginning in the preschool years lays a sound foundation for the elementary years. A difficult beginning is more likely to result in complications in the later stages.

Underline the four principles in the paragraphs above. Now complete the following statements referring to the text.

1. The order of development is _____

_____

2. The rate of development _____

_____

3. Development proceeds _____

_____

God created us in His image, but the physical, social, and spiritual environment either nourishes or impoverishes the development of our spiritual selves. How we develop spiritually depends to a large extent on how others welcome us into the world and shape the world in which we live. Our primary welcomers and shapers are our parents.

Developmental Stages

Parents find that the stages of development provide helpful pictures of what their children experience. Remember that these are summaries of what can be expected; no child conforms precisely to these expectations. Think of your own children as you read the following descriptions.

Infancy (Birth - Two Years)

The infant enters this world learning primarily through sensory experiences of taste, touch, sound, sight, and smell. The child learns her first lessons about the nature of God through her experience with those who care (or do not care) for her. Learning to trust parents is basic for all relationships with others and with God.

The Preschool Child (Ages 2-5)

Preschoolers are trying to do more things for themselves and make choices within limits. Children develop independence because they feel secure in the parents' love. They are taking first steps from self-centeredness to God-centeredness. People must first know themselves before they can give themselves back to God.

Early Childhood (Ages 6-9)

Rules become increasingly important. The child obeys the rules to avoid parents' and teachers' disapproval and gain acceptance and love. As children ask hard questions, they cause us to reexamine our cherished values and our faith. This requires openness on our part to explore with them rather than to discourage their attempt to understand the world of the family, school, and church.

Late Childhood (Ages 10-11)

Older children take on more responsibility for their behavior and do what they ought to do because it is right. They are less dependent on rewards or punishment to shape their behavior. Their faith is becoming their own rather than something mediated through parents. Although each child is unique, this is the age most children desire to make a commitment to Jesus Christ.

Parents lay the groundwork for this decision as they encourage independence, critical thinking, and responsibility for themselves. This comes, of course, with a great deal of support and guidance from Mom and Dad.

Adolescence (Ages 12-17)

The quiet of the school-age years changes dramatically with the onset of puberty. Rules accepted at eleven now seem binding. Periods of turbulence and upheaval alternate with confidence and sunshine. Along with the radical physical changes, radical changes take place in teens' cognitive or thinking abilities. For the first time, the growing child thinks in abstract terms.

Teenagers struggle with the apparent contradictions between what is and what ought to be. Many rebel against authority as they seek answers for themselves.

Parenting by grace calls for parents of teenagers to encourage their growing independence, recognize that rebellion is a part of development, and understand that teenagers need to take responsiblity for as much of their lives as they can handle. At the same time, parents understand that teenagers need guidance and reasonable limits.

Refer back to your own child's developmental stage. Underline key words and phrases that characterize the stage. Do this for each of your children.

Parental Responsibility for Children's Development

It has been said that the foundation for a child's life is laid in the first three years, and most of the building of that life occurs in the years before adulthood. Parents, therefore, carry the major responsibility for the physical, emotional, moral, and spiritual growth of their children. To parent by grace, parents need basically to know three persons: their child, themselves, and God. No small assignment! Let us examine these three.

Knowing Your Child

The major portion of this session provides a brief overview of the development of children. Most parents find it helpful to know what is normal for each stage of development. It helps to know that teens criticize the actions of their parents as not being consistent with their statements of faith. This is normal, even though uncomfortable for parents. Knowing what to expect, parents can prepare. Understanding children's development provides a perspective on behavior that helps parents see the larger picture instead of being caught up in a whirlpool of self-doubt and overreaction to what may be an important, but passing, phase of development. The references at the end of this lesson provide more background in children's spiritual and moral development.

At the same time, no two children develop the same way. Parents need to understand their individual children as well as know what most children are like. The best informant for the parent in understanding the child is the child himself. Parents need to listen, observe, ask questions, and listen some more.

Refer to the nine principles of discipline and guidance in the "Summary" of lesson 2 on page 33. Write the three principles that especially help a parent to know his or her child.

a. _____

b. _____

c. _____

Knowing Yourself

Children learn from stories, and the story they will know and remember the most—which shapes their lives—is the story enacted in front of them, the lives of their parents. If you want to know what your child is learning about the spiritual and moral dimension of life, look at what you are teaching through example.

Children learn, not by what we say, but by what they see. Parents need to be clear about what they value in their lives and how those values show in their daily actions. Parents need to involve themselves and their families in ministry events which describe in picture language to their children the meaning of Christian faith. Parents need to share in the fellowship of the church where they can find support in their struggles from other parents and can find other models of living faith for their children. Finally, parents need to parent their children as gifts of God, unique and of great worth. In this way, they parent their children as God parents them, a living demonstration of the love of God.

Refer to your ranking of the priorities in your life on page 25. Rank them again, this time according to your ideal—the way you would *like* for them to be. What changes would need to be made in your life in order for the ideal to be realized? (No written response is necessary.)

Knowing God

To parent children as God parents us, we must have a living relationship with God and a firm foundation in the Bible. Our lives must be lived as a living testimony to our faith (Deut. 6:5-9). Only when we know the grace of God in our lives can we truly parent by grace.

Spend a few minutes evaluating your life in relationship to God. Write a number from the scale in the blank beside each statement.

Strong No						Strong Yes
1	2	3	4	5	6	7

_____ a. I have a very personal and meaningful relationship with God.

_____ b. My life is characterized by steady spiritual growth.

_____ c. I find it easy to pray each day.

_____ d. I use the Bible in seeking guidance for my life.

_____ e. I am faithful to Christ in every area of my life.

_____ f. My life is a good model for my children.

List the names of three persons a parent must know in order to parent by grace.

1. _____ 2. _____ 3. _____

Needs of Children

All Children

Parental evaluation of children's development will vary according to the needs of each child. Some of the needs remain basically the same for a lifetime. Other needs become apparent as the child develops or as unusual circumstances (e.g., divorce and remarriage) occur. As you review the needs of the various age groups, evaluate how well your child(ren)'s needs are being met. Circle a number for each need to indicate the degree to which it is being met by each child. Use a different color pen for each child. Identification of aspects of your child's development needing your attention is the first step toward meeting those needs.

Preschoolers need to:	Not at all				To a great extent
Grow intellectually, physically, emotionally, socially, and spiritually.	1	2	3	4	5
Grow in self-esteem through being accepted and affirmed.	1	2	3	4	5
Be disciplined effectively and constructively.	1	2	3	4	5
Be encouraged in their beginning interests and abilities.	1	2	3	4	5
Accept and communicate their feelings.	1	2	3	4	5
Have realistic expectations and guidelines set for their behavior.	1	2	3	4	5
Learn how to relate to others.	1	2	3	4	5
Be related to as different, unique, and special.	1	2	3	4	5
Learn appropriate sexual terminology and observe positive models of sexual identity.	1	2	3	4	5
Observe positive models of moral behavior and spiritual growth.	1	2	3	4	5
Develop through creative play.	1	2	3	4	5
Begin to understand the world in which they live.	1	2	3	4	5
Begin to understand and respond to God's love.	1	2	3	4	5

Extent my child's needs are being met

Elementary-age children need to:	Extent my child's needs are being met				
	Not at all				To a great extent
• Grow intellectually, physically, emotionally, socially, and spiritually.	1	2	3	4	5
• Be guided toward a personal relationship with God through Jesus Christ as Savior and Lord.	1	2	3	4	5
• Grow in self-esteem through being accepted and affirmed.	1	2	3	4	5
• Be disciplined effectively and constructively.	1	2	3	4	5
• Be encouraged in their beginning interests and abilities.	1	2	3	4	5
• Accept and communicate their feelings.	1	2	3	4	5
• Have realistic expectations and guidelines set for their behavior.	1	2	3	4	5
• Learn how to relate to others.	1	2	3	4	5
• Be treated as different, unique, and special.	1	2	3	4	5
• Learn appropriate sexual terminology and develop sexual identity.	1	2	3	4	5
• Observe positive models of moral behavior and spiritual growth.	1	2	3	4	5
• Appreciate the importance of work and play.	1	2	3	4	5
• Develop and maintain friendships.	1	2	3	4	5
• Grow in their understanding of the world in which they live.	1	2	3	4	5

Adolescents need to:	Extent my child's needs are being met				
	Not at all				To a great extent
• Grow intellectually, physically, emotionally, socially, and spiritually.	1	2	3	4	5
• Build self-esteem through affirmation and acceptance.	1	2	3	4	5
• Discover and develop their gifts and abilities.	1	2	3	4	5
• Grow toward spiritual maturity and accept responsibility for Christian discipleship.	1	2	3	4	5
• Develop self-discipline, which involves being personally responsible for decision making and independence.	1	2	3	4	5
• Handle moral and ethical decisions, including the influence of the media.	1	2	3	4	5
• Develop positive interpersonal relationships with others, including their peers, the opposite sex, their families, and authority.	1	2	3	4	5
• Accept and communicate their emotions in positive, constructive ways.	1	2	3	4	5
• Be helped to prepare for marriage and new roles in family living.	1	2	3	4	5
• Behave out of a wholesome attitude of sexual identity.	1	2	3	4	5
• Be helped to recognize their limitations and develop realistic expectations.	1	2	3	4	5
• Become aware of opportunities for missions/ministry with their families and churches.	1	2	3	4	5
• Be guided in career decisions.	1	2	3	4	5
• Develop personal/family celebrations and worship.	1	2	3	4	5
• Grow in understanding the world in which they live and their place in it.	1	2	3	4	5

Special Children

This category goes across age and stage development to focus on the unique needs of special children. By definition, special children have physical, mental, and/or emotional handicaps or gifts. The needs identified in this category supplement the needs itemized in the age group of the special child. For example, an eight-year-old with muscular dystrophy would have needs in the children's category as well as in this category.

In addition to the needs of their age group, *special children* need to:	Extent my child's needs are being met				
	Not at all				To a great extent
• Build self-esteem in response to unique challenges.	1	2	3	4	5
• Accept and communicate emotions.	1	2	3	4	5
• Accept limitations and develop realistic expectations.	1	2	3	4	5
• Develop healthy relationships with others.	1	2	3	4	5
• Discover and develop gifts and abilities to the fullest potential.	1	2	3	4	5
• Develop appropriate levels of independence.	1	2	3	4	5

Children of Single-Parent Families

A single-parent family system is formed either through the death of a marriage partner, divorce, separation, or desertion. It also occurs when an unmarried person becomes a parent through giving birth or adoption, foster parenting, or when an unwed person assumes the responsibility for rearing a child without the help of a partner. In addition to the needs of their age-group, children of single-parent families have unique needs.

In addition to the needs of their age group, *children in single-parent families* need to:	Extent my child's needs are being met				
	Not at all				To a great extent
• Build self-esteem in response to family crises.	1	2	3	4	5
• Develop a sense of security and support systems for the family.	1	2	3	4	5
• Accept and communicate strong feelings in a positive, healthy, and constructive way.	1	2	3	4	5
• Understand that parents may have certain restrictions to abide by in legal arrangements.	1	2	3	4	5
• Maintain appropriate contact with relatives.	1	2	3	4	5
• Maintain significant family rituals.	1	2	3	4	5
• Be prepared for parents marrying again.	1	2	3	4	5

Children of Blended Families

The blended family is faced with a wide range of additional issues. Many of the problems in a blended family are in the areas of relationships and communication. New relationships make underlying problems of communication acute and apparent. In addition to the needs of their age group, children of blended families have unique needs.

In addition to the needs of their age group, *children in blended families* need to:	Extent my child's needs are being met				
	Not at all				To a great extent
• Be accepted, accept new family members, and develop healthy emotions toward the new family.	1	2	3	4	5
• Understand the similarities and differences in values of the two newly-merged families.	1	2	3	4	5

• Handle the unique conflicts that are inherent in blended family units in a positive, creative manner.	1	2	3	4	5
• Receive consistent discipline.	1	2	3	4	5
• Have smooth visitation situations.	1	2	3	4	5
• Have the new parenting team form a united front.	1	2	3	4	5
• Have perceptive parents who respect the children's legacy from the past.	1	2	3	4	5
• Develop other support systems in addition to the new family unit.	1	2	3	4	5
• Have handled competently any legal ramifications of the blended family, such as adoption, wills, marriage between step-siblings, etc.	1	2	3	4	5

Obviously, you are thankful for those areas in which your child's needs are being met and his development seems to be proceeding smoothly. As unmet needs are identified, consult with a trusted friend, counselor, minister, or your child's teachers. In some cases, additional professional evaluations and recommendations are advisable.

Checkpoint
Review time. Complete the following exercises.

1. Define *growth, maturation,* and *learning* by placing the number corresponding to the correct definition in the blank beside each term.

_____ a. growth   (1) a change in environment

_____ b. maturation (2) a change in behavior or attitude

_____ c. learning   (3) a spiritual change

                        (4) a qualitative change

                        (5) a quantitative change

2. State four principles of child development.

   a. _____

   b. _____

   c. _____

   d. _____

3. Identify the developmental stage of each of your children and describe briefly the typical characteristics of the stage. Use a separate sheet of paper for your work.

4. Name three persons a parent must know in order to parent by grace.

   a. _____ *b.* _____ *c.* _____

5. Refer again to the list of developmental needs of children (pages 38-41). Identify the ones to which you need to give special attention in order to help your children in their development. Do this for each child. Use separate sheets of paper for your work.

6. State two specific actions you can take to help your children more effectively in their development.

   a. _____

   b. _____

Check your work with the "Summary" on page 42.

Reflection and Application.
1. Reflect upon the number of "I" messages and "you" messages you gave your child(ren) this past week. Is the number of "you" messages decreasing?

2. Continue your practice of affirmation and celebration. Look for a behavior or action by each child this week over which you can express affirmation and celebration. Complete the chart.

Child's name	Child's action	Affirmation and celebration

3. Continue your use of methods of discipline and guidance, other than punishment, with your child(ren). Complete the chart at the top of the next page, page 42.

Child's name	Method of Discipline and Guidance (other than punishment)	Immediate results

4. Spend a few minutes reflecting on the following question. (No written response is necessary.)

a. How would you explain the four principles of child development to a neighbor?

• The order of development varies little from one child to another.

• The rate of development varies greatly from one child to another.

• Development proceeds in stages and each stage has characteristic traits.

• Development is cumulative.

b. In what ways have you seen the principles of child development demonstrated in the lives of your children?

c. Are the stages of child development helpful to you in understanding your own child(ren)? What are some ways in which your child(ren) differ from the typical characteristics of the stages?

Summary

1. Growth is quantitative change; maturation is qualitative change.

2. Learning is change in behavior or attitude.

3. Principles of child development:

• The order of development varies little from one child to another.

• The rate of development varies greatly from one child to another.

• Development proceeds in stages, and each stage has characteristic traits.

• Development is cumulative.

4. There are five developmental stages: infancy (birth-2 years), preschool (ages 2-5), early childhood (ages 6-9), late childhood (ages 10-11), and adolescence (ages 12-17).

5. Parents are responsible for the development of their children. To parent by grace, parents need to know their child, themselves, and God.

6. Every child has some basic needs at each level of development.

7. Children with mental and/or emotional handicaps or gifts, children of single-parent families, and children of blended families have unique needs that go across age and stage development categories.

Looking Ahead

Lesson 4 focuses on discipline again and builds on the concepts of discipline presented in lesson 2. The title of the lesson is "Discipline Grows Children in the Way They Should Go."

In addition to reading lesson 4, complete the following activity.

The long-term goal of parental discipline is to bring children to the point of self-discipline rather than relying upon external discipline. Observe and describe a situation where your child's behavior—

• depended upon external discipline _____

_____

_____

• demonstrated self-discipline _____

_____

_____

Describe your feelings about your child's behavior in

each situation. _____

_____

_____

Lesson 4

Discipline Grows Children in the Way They Should Go

The Purpose of Parenting by Grace

Looking Back

Overview

Learning Goals

The Value of Discipline in Parenting

More Basic Principles of Discipline

Parental Responsibility in Discipline

Causes of Behavioral Patterns

Using the Principles of Discipline

Checkpoint

Reflection and Application

Summary

Looking Ahead

Looking Back

Lesson 3 focused on the physical, moral, and spiritual development of children. The purpose of the lesson was to help you better understand your own children. Four basic principles of child development were given and the developmental stages of children were described. The importance of giving attention to children's developmental needs was emphasized. Turn to the "Summary" on page 42 and review the lesson.

You prepared for lesson 4 by identifying specific situations where your child's behavior depended upon external or outside discipline and also situations where your child demonstrated self-discipline. Review the evaluation you did on page 42. Reflect on actions you can take to guide your child toward self-discipline.

Overview

This lesson returns to the subject of discipline. Since the name of the course is Parenting by Grace: Discipline and Spiritual Growth, you can expect a strong emphasis on discipline throughout the lessons. Discipline is teaching and guidance and cannot be emphasized too much. The value of discipline as it relates to the development of the child is noted in this lesson, and five additional principles of discipline are examined. Parental responsibility for discipline is emphasized. You will practice identifying the causes of a child's behavior and implementing some of the principles of discipline.

Learning Goals

After completing this lesson, you should have a better understanding of the use of discipline in parenting.

You will be able to—

• summarize in your own words the value of discipline in parenting;

• state five additional basic principles of discipline not discussed in lesson 2;

• summarize briefly in your own words what the Bible teaches concerning parental responsibility for discipline;

• identify the cause of one behavioral problem or pattern of your child previously identified in lesson 2;

• implement at least two basic principles of discipline with your child.

43

The Value of Discipline in Parenting

Let's begin by looking briefly at a biblical perspective of the value of discipline in the home. Discipline grows children in the way they should go. Proverbs 22:6 reads: "Train a child in the way he should go, and when he is old he will not turn from it" (NIV).

Good discipline encourages each person to find himself in God. Parents don't always know what God's purpose is for their children. But we can help our children grow spiritually in ways that will help them find that purpose for themselves. We should dedicate our children to the Lord to be used in His service, in whatever way He chooses.

Discipline helps children to learn self-discipline—how to discipline themselves. Rather than simply responding to discipline imposed by another person, children need to learn how to trust in God and guide and control their lives through His Spirit. God's plan for His highest and best creation includes placing children with parents so that parents will love and nurture the children until they can function on their own.

Read again the three paragraphs above. Underline one sentence in each paragraph that states a value of discipline.

Why is self-discipline of greater value than discipline from the outside? _____

_____

_____

Summarize in your own words the value of discipline in the life of a child. _____

_____

_____

_____

More Basic Principles of Discipline

Lesson 2 emphasized nine principles of discipline and guidance:

- **Try to understand children's development in general and your child's development in particular.**
- **Be a sensitive listener to your child.**
- **Be a good observer of your child's behavior.**
- **Speak kindly, quietly, and yet firmly.**
- **Speak on the child's level of understanding.**
- **Child-proof the environment so that more time and attention is focused on children than on material items.**

- **Identify appropriate limits that reassure and guide children.**
- **Consistently maintain necessary limits.**
- **Encourage children's development of freedom within limits.**

There are no easy answers or definite rules to make us loving, merciful parents. Parenting by grace is an attitude. We can understand more clearly our role as agents of God's grace as we study Luke 2:52: "And Jesus increased in wisdom and stature, and in favour with God and man." Because of this verse and because of the way Jesus lived as an adult, we can see evidence that Mary and Joseph understood and practiced principles of discipline related to growth and maturity.

In addition to the principles listed above, additional principles or guidelines are helpful.

1. *Encourage a child's feelings of self-worth and self-esteem.* This is an attitude that says to the child: "You are special. You are God's creation. He made you and gave you to me to love and guide."

When and how did you last affirm and encourage your child's feelings of self-worth? _____

_____

2. *Guide children toward self-discipline and self-control by administering discipline and love with forgiveness and reconciliation.*

What is one thing you do to help your children develop self-discipline? _____

_____

Evaluate your child(ren) in the area of self-discipline. Place an X on the scale to indicate where your child would be between parental discipline and self-discipline. Use a different color pen for each child.

Guided by parental discipline	Guided by self-discipline
├──────────────────────────────────────┤	

3. *Teach a child to relate appropriately to others in the family and those at school, church, and in the neighborhood.*

Again, it is an attitude that says, "I care about people." As parents model this attitude, children will learn that ministry, friendship, gratitude, and thoughtfulness are part of the Christian life.

Evaluate your child(ren) in the area of relating to others. Place an X on the scale beside each quality to indicate how your child rates. Use a different color pen for each child.

	weak	strong
friendship	⊢————————⊣	
thoughtfulness	⊢————————⊣	
gratitude	⊢————————⊣	
caring concern	⊢————————⊣	
helpfulness	⊢————————⊣	

4. *Help a child grow toward emotional maturity.*

The emotionally mature person is someone whose life gives evidence of the qualities of love, joy, peace, patience, kindness, goodness, gentleness, and self-control (Gal. 5:22-23).

Evaluate your child(ren) in the area of emotional maturity. Place an *X* on the scale beside each quality for each child. Use different color pens.

	weak	strong
love	⊢————————⊣	
joy	⊢————————⊣	
peace	⊢————————⊣	
patience	⊢————————⊣	
gentleness	⊢————————⊣	

5. *Help a child grow toward his potential in spiritual and moral development.*

All of life influences the spiritual and moral development of a child. His parents' example, his early training in the church, his own understanding of God's love, and the urging of the Holy Spirit will draw a child to a relationship with Christ. This is the goal of Christian parenting: to bring children to mature, responsible Christian living.

Reflect upon the spiritual and moral development of your children. What are the key factors that influence their development positively?

_____

_____

What are some factors that influence your children's spiritual and moral development negatively? _____

_____

Underline the five principles of discipline discussed in the preceding section. Analyze each principle and circle what you consider to be the key word or term in each principle.

The key words or terms I selected are listed below. (They are not listed in the order they appear in the text.) Using them as hints, write each principle.

emotional_____

_____

relate_____

_____

self-discipline_____

_____

spiritual_____

_____

self-worth_____

_____

Check your work to make sure you understand the five principles. Read each principle again and reflect upon how you could explain the principle to a neighbor.

Parental Responsibility for Discipline

Read the following Bible passages. Summarize in your own words what each one teaches about parental responsibility for disciplining children.

Deuteronomy 6:5-9 _____

_____

_____

Proverbs 19:18 _____

_____

_____

Proverbs 22:6 _____

_____

Hebrews 12:7-11 _____

_____

_____

As parents we need to be reminded that although parenting is a difficult task, we are not in it alone. God offers to each of us the same love, affirmation, discipline, and guidance that He wants us to give our children. A right relationship with God can strengthen and encourage parents in their task of disciplining and guiding their children.

Parents have the opportunity to participate in their child's life. Guiding a child toward a conversion experience, baptism and church membership, and continued Christian growth is both a major responsibility and a major source of joy and pleasure for a Christian parent. Sharing these special events and intense feelings that accompany them adds depth and meaning to the parent-child relationship.

The Bible is practical and relevant for parents today. Although the Bible does not speak the languages of our highly technical age, the principles found in the Bible are ageless and speak eloquently to every aspect of today's life. Parents can look with confidence to the Bible as the primary source of guidance and encouragement for their task.

God teaches us how to discipline. God's grace models good discipline for Christian parents. God's grace teaches us how to forgive and lead our children to improve their behavior. That means we correct our children and sometimes punish them. But we do it out of our love for them. God said of His relationship with David, "I will be his father, and he will be my son. When he does wrong, I will punish him with the rod of men, with floggings inflicted by men. But my love will never be taken away from him" (2 Sam. 7:14-15, NIV).

God gave us the perfect example of unconditional love in Jesus Christ. Before we even knew Him, God loved us and sent His Son for our redemption, to be our guide and our salvation. We can never love our children as God has loved us, but He is our model. God teaches us how to discipline by grace, and that grace involves two ingredients: guidance and unearned love.

What, then do we set before ourselves as our goal in disciplining our children? Write your goal in two or three sentences. _____

_____

_____

_____

Now write a brief prayer asking God to help you achieve this goal. _____

_____

_____

_____

We want our children to grow up spiritually. We want them to be self-disciplined, mature, and have a strong relationship with God, their loving Heavenly Father. We want them to experience the grace of God in their relationship with us, their parents. That is a worthy goal!

As we aim to develop self-discipline in our children, we teach it by showing it in our lives. God's grace teaches us self-discipline. In Titus 2:11-13 (NIV), we read:

For the grace of God that brings salvation has appeared to all men. It teaches us to say "No" to ungodliness and worldly passions, and to live self-controlled, upright and godly lives in this present age, while we wait for the blessed hope.

How does God teach us self-discipline? By the life of Jesus Christ. He is our example of self-discipline. Of course, we can never measure up to His example. We make mistakes as parents. Children learn, though, even by how we handle our mistakes. What is important? The direction of our lives. Even if we make mistakes, our parenting needs to be headed in the direction of showing grace to our children by how we handle ourselves. We discipline, then, by showing self-discipline.

Reflect for a few minutes on your responsibility for your children. What is the role of the following in the discipline and guidance of your children? Refer to the preceding section as needed.

Bible _____

_____

God's grace _____

_____

unconditional love _____

_____

punishment _____

_____

self-discipline _____

Jesus Christ_____

_____

Summarize briefly the biblical teachings concerning your responsibility as parents for disciplining your child(ren). _____

_____

_____

Causes of Behavioral Patterns

Observing children's behavior has been previously identified as a significant principle of discipline. As you observe a child's behavior, try to understand the cause of the behavior. Ask yourself, Why does she feel like hitting her sister? Why does he no longer want to participate in the children's choir? Why is she so eager to shop for clothes that are identical to her friend's clothes? Look behind the action for the cause.

Understanding the cause of the child's behavior is a good beginning for appropriate discipline—discipline that enhances spiritual development. We need to develop a sensitivity to being able to identify causes of behavioral patterns.

Read the following situations. Suggest the probable cause(s) of the child's behavior. How does the parental discipline indicated influence the child's development, especially spiritual and moral development?

Situation	Cause(s) of behavior	Influence of the discipline on development
1. Mom and Dad tell four-year-old Sue she is a lazy slowpoke when she takes too long to put on her sandals.		
2. Mom spanks two-year-old Mark's hand every time he reaches for the china teapot displayed on the coffee table.		
3. Mom gives five-year-old Ryan a chance to explain why he was fighting on the playground.		
4. Mom and Dad fuss at eight-month-old Abbey for crying and say, "Naughty girl."		
5. Mom tells four-year-old Barbara, "We don't know how birds can fly. Let's find a book that will tell us."		
6. Mom threatens three-year-old Carol. "If you pull your sister's hair again, I'll spank you."		
7. Dad refuses to let ten-year-old Shawn watch television for two days after he lied about having no homework.		
8. Mom and Dad nag at nine-year-old Betsy every morning to get her out of bed for breakfast.		
9. Mom gives in and lets eleven-year-old Cindy watch an *R*-rated movie.		

"She knows it is just pretend. It won't hurt her just this once," she says.		
10. Mom shouts at ten-year-old Martin, "You are just plain dumb. All *D*'s. What's wrong with you?"		
11. Dad talks with six-year-old Lisa about why she has a stomachache every morning when it is time for school.		
12. Mom and Dad answer nine-year-old Jane's questions about sex honestly and openly.		
13. Mom insists that seventeen-year-old Connie pay for her speeding tickets with her own money.		
14. Mom and Dad encourage fifteen-year-old Jeff in his desire to get an after-school job.		
15. Dad forbids sixteen-year-old Betsy to date Tom because he is not a Christian.		

In the previous situations, was the child's behavior often typical of his age group? How had appropriate or inappropriate behavior been taught to the child? (No written response is necessary.)

Identify two behavioral problems or patterns of your child and analyze what you think is the cause of the behavior.

Behavior	Probable Cause(s) of Behavior

Using the Principles of Discipline

Learning to parent by grace can be compared to

learning to ride a bicycle. You fall a lot at first, but you learn to balance the more you ride. Occasionally you still take a nasty fall. No parent ever becomes the perfect parent. As you practice loving, affirming, disciplining, and guiding, you get better and better. You still make mistakes, but you have only to ask for God's forgiveness and try again.

Read the following situations. Assume that you are the parent involved. How could you handle each situation to enhance and encourage your child's spiritual development?

Situation 1

The bedtime ritual is finished: bath, pajamas, water, story, bathroom, prayers, and a goodnight kiss. You tuck your four-year-old in bed and whisper, "I love you. Sleep well." You turn off the lights and walk slowly, quietly from the room. Two minutes later you hear, "Mom, I can't sleep." "Daddy, it's too dark in here." You make a trip to the bedroom. You give another kiss, another pat. Five minutes later, "Mom, I'm hot." "Daddy, I see something in the corner." Again you go to the bedroom. For ten to fifteen minutes this scene is repeated. Then the crying starts. You get up from your chair and start toward the bedroom.

What are your feelings and what is the first response you would like to make? _____

_____

How would your first response likely affect your pre-

schooler? _____

_____

How could you respond with discipline which en-

hances your preschooler's spiritual development? _____

_____

How would this discipline likely affect your pre-

schooler? _____

_____

Situation 2
The television is blaring reruns. Because of soccer practice and swim classes, supper is late. Everyone is tired. You ask one child to take out the garbage. Immediately you hear, "But I did it yesterday. It's Sue's turn today."

"No, it isn't either. We swapped jobs. You said that you would take out the garbage for two days in a row if I would dry the dishes last night."

"I did not say that, either. I said . . ."

You have heard enough. You march into the den.

What are your feelings and what is the first response

you would like to make? _____

_____

How would your first response likely affect your chil-

dren? _____

_____

How could you respond with discipline which en-

hances your elementary-age children's spiritual de-

velopment? _____

_____

How would this discipline likely affect your children?

_____

Situation 3
You meet a friend while shopping. Your friend says, "I

saw your daughter last week. She is a beautiful girl. I know you must be proud of her." You smile and accept her kind words. Then she says, "But if I were you, I would keep an eye on those kids she was with. My husband and I do not allow our daughter to hang around with them."

Later at home you think about what your friend said. When your daughter gets home from school, she says, "School is boring; I can't wait to meet my friends."

What are your feelings and what is the first response

you would like to make? _____

_____

How would your first response likely affect your teen-

ager? _____

_____

How could you respond with discipline which en-

hances your teenager's spiritual development? _____

_____

_____

How would this discipline likely affect your teenager?

_____

_____

Parenting by grace is more than a new phrase, another good idea, or even a Baptist program. It is a way of life, a life-style, and a decision. It is an attitude that comes when you accept God's gift of grace and pass it along to others, specifically your children.

Checkpoint
This review covers the main points in the lesson.

1. Summarize briefly in your own words the value of discipline in parenting.

_____

_____

_____

2. State the five basic principles of parenting discussed in this lesson.

a. _____

_____

b. _____

_____

c. _____

_____

d. _____

_____

e. _____

_____

3. Summarize briefly in your own words what the Bible teaches concerning parental responsibility for discipline. _____

_____

_____

Check your work with the answers in the "Summary."

Reflection and Application

1. Refer to the behavioral problem or pattern of your child that you identified in lesson 2, page 33. Identify what you think is the probable cause of this behavior.

_____

_____

2. Refer again to the behavioral problem in number 1 above. Refer also to the plans you outlined in lesson 2 for disciplining your child for this behavior. Make any revisions needed in your plans for discipline in light of this lesson. Try to make use of at least three of the five principles of discipline discussed in this lesson.

3. How well do you practice the principles of discipline with your children? Score your report card with a letter grade for each principle.

A—Excellent; B—Good; C—Fair; D—Poor; F—Failed.

Principles from Lesson 2

_____ 1. I understand my child's development.
_____ 2. I listen to my children.
_____ 3. I am a good observer.
_____ 4. I speak kindly, quietly, yet firmly.
_____ 5. I speak on my child's level.
_____ 6. My house is child proofed.
_____ 7. I identify appropriate limits.
_____ 8. I am consistent in maintaining necessary limits.
_____ 9. I encourage my children's development of freedom within limits.

Principles from Lesson 4

_____ 1. I encourage my child's feelings of self-worth and self-esteem.
_____ 2. I guide my children toward self-discipline and self-control.
_____ 3. I teach my children to relate appropriately to others.
_____ 4. I help my children grow toward emotional maturity.
_____ 5. I help my children grow toward their potential in spiritual and moral development.

Spend a few minutes thinking of ways you can improve in any area where your grade is C or lower.

4. Continue your practice of affirmation and celebration. Look for a behavior or action by each child this week over which you can express affirmation and celebration. Complete the chart.

Child's name	Child's action	Affirmation and celebration

5. Plan to use at least two basic principles of discipline with your children this week. Complete the chart.

Child's name	Principle of discipline	How I used the principle

6. Review the section, "Causes of Behavioral Patterns" on pages 47-48. Read again each of the fifteen situations involving discipline or lack of it. If the situation is an example of parenting by grace, place a (✓) beside it; if it is not an example of parenting by grace, place an X beside it.

For the situations that are not examples of parenting by grace, think of a more suitable type of parental behavior in response to the child's inappropriate behavior.

(I checked as examples of parenting by grace items 3, 5, 7, 11, 12, 13, 14, 15.)

7. Spend a few minutes reflecting on the following questions. (No written response is necessary.)

• How does parental discipline help children learn self-discipline?

• How well did your parents implement the principles of discipline with you when you were growing up?

• How were your own feelings of self-worth and self-esteem as a child encouraged by others?

• What were some of the key things in your own life that helped you to develop self-discipline?

• What is a problem you have in teaching your child to relate well to others?

• What was the single greatest influence on your spiritual development when you were growing up?

Summary

1. Discipline grows children in the way they should go. It encourages each person to find himself in God and helps him learn self-discipline.

2. Five additional principles of discipline:

• Encourage a child's feelings of self-worth and self-esteem.

• Guide children toward self-discipline and self-control.

• Teach a child to relate appropriately to others.

• Help a child grow toward emotional maturity.

• Help a child grow toward his potential in spiritual and moral development.

3. The Bible teaches that parents are responsible for the discipline and guidance of their children. Parents should give their children love, affirmation, teaching, and correction. Parents should guide them toward maturity and self-discipline.

4. Understanding the cause of a child's behavior is necessary for appropriate discipline.

Looking Ahead

Lesson 5 centers on the use of discipline to affirm appropriate behavior. Complete the following activities as you prepare for the lesson.

1. Think about your child right now. Affirming his strengths is a good way to discipline your child. List at least four traits or strengths your child possesses that you would like to affirm or encourage. (For example, friendliness, an inquiring mind, appreciation for beauty, etc.) Use separate sheets of paper for more than one child.

a. _____

b. _____

c. _____

d. _____

2. Begin thinking of specific actions you can take to affirm and encourage these traits in your child. You will be asked later to implement these actions.

Unit Three

How to Discipline by Grace

Lesson 5
Discipline Affirms Appropriate Behavior

Looking Back

Overview

Learning Goals

Appropriate Behavior Defined

Affirming Appropriate Behavior

Methods of Reinforcing Appropriate Behavior

Checkpoint

Reflection and Application

Summary

Looking Ahead

Looking Back
Lesson 4 dealt with the value of discipline and parental responsibility for discipline. Attention was given to identifying causes of behavioral problems. The lesson centered around five basic principles of discipline related to self-esteem, self-control, relating to others, and emotional, moral, and spiritual development. Turn to the "Summary" on page 51 and review the lesson.

Overview
This lesson deals with the use of discipline in affirming appropriate behavior. Appropriate behavior is defined and specific examples of parents affirming appropriate behavior are described. Eight methods of affirming appropriate behavior are explained in detail.

Learning Goals
After completing this lesson, you should have a better understanding of how to use discipline to affirm appropriate behavior.

You will be able to—
• define appropriate behavior and name three factors upon which appropriate behavior depends;
• state at least five methods of reinforcing appropriate behavior;
• identify and reinforce at least three appropriate behaviors in your child(ren) this week.

Appropriate Behavior Defined
Check *agree* or *disagree* after each statement. The statements are not necessarily true or false, but you should be able to indicate whether you agree or disagree with them.

	Agree	Disagree
1. Appropriate behavior is a matter of moral absolutes and does not depend upon parental expectations.	☐	☐
2. It is a mistake for parents to hold different expectations of appropriate behavior for different children.	☐	☐
3. Cultural expectations and norms have created artificial differences between appropriate behavior for boys and girls.	☐	☐
4. There are God-given differences between the sexes, and parents should seek to enhance, not minimize, these differences.	☐	☐
5. What is considered appropriate behavior for children varies with the parent.	☐	☐

Check your work as you read this section.

What is appropriate behavior? *Appropriate* may be defined as suitable, acceptable, or meeting certain expectations. If your child's actions and attitudes are acceptable to you, than you consider the behavior appropriate.

Appropriate behavior obviously depends on the child, the parent, and the specific situation or occasion.

The Child

The developmental level of the child needs to be taken into account in determining appropriate behavior. Actions that would be considered acceptable or even commendable for your toddler might be inappropriate for your eight-year-old.

A toddler who holds on to his teddy bear and says, "Mine," may be supported in his newly acquired verbal skills. You might say, "Yes, that is your teddy bear." To your eight-year-old, you might say: "Jennifer, I think Andy wants to look at your teddy bear. Andy will hold it carefully and return it to you."

Acknowledging unique characteristics of children may be interpreted as having different definitions of appropriate behavior for each child. For example, if your fourteen-year-old has a late dress rehearsal for the church musical, completing her homework after 10:00 PM may be appropriate behavior. Her twelve-year-old sister who watches television until 10:00 PM before starting her homework is behaving inappropriately.

Write your response to this question: Should appropriate behavior be defined differently for girls and boys?

• For example, should you expect your son to be more physically active and boisterous than your daughter?

• For example, should you expect your daughter to display more warm and nurturing behavior than boys her age?

Traditional concepts of masculinity and femininity draw neat, clean, definite lines between appropriate behavior for boys and girls. In turn, men's and women's lives have distinctive characteristics.

More developmental concepts of masculinity and femininity acknowledge the physical and biological basis for certain differences in boys' and girls' behavior. Our own expectations contribute greatly to other differences between the sexes.

The Parent

Parents are the primary influence in many aspects of children's development. Parents model their interpretation of appropriate behavior as a male or female. Children learn from models in the family as well as models presented in the media, in the church, and in the neighborhood.

What is considered appropriate behavior for children varies with the parent, grandparent, teacher, or neighbor of a child. Although we could initially agree on common expectations regarding manners, homework, and chores, very quickly different expectations of children emerge. As a result of our previous experiences, we each define appropriate behavior in unique ways.

What is one way the expectations of your parents enhanced your development as a son or daughter?

Did the expectations of your parents limit your development in any way? If so, how?

In what ways do you believe your expectations as a parent enhance your children's development?

Is there any way in which your expectations as a parent may be limiting your children's behavior? If so, how?

The importance of consistent expectations for children have been identified as a key principle of discipline. In many areas of children's lives, they are confronted with inconsistent expectations regarding appropriate behavior. Hopefully the key adults involved with a child can agree on basic standards of appropriate behavior.

Agreeing on appropriate behavior may require adults to negotiate their positions and expectations. Dad may need help to see the importance of baby feeding himself although it is messier and more time consuming than Dad feeding the baby. Mom may need help accepting the fact that a few scraped knees seem to be inevitable for an eight-year-old practicing soccer with the team. Grandparents may need assistance in understanding appropriate hairstyles or dress for teens. Will Ted's English teacher understand his request to read and research a topic other than the subjects on the approved list?

What is one way you have negotiated and changed your expectations in the past concerning appropriate behavior for your child? _____

_____

The Specific Situation

Defining appropriate behavior depends not only on the children and parents but also on the specific situation or occasion. Can you remember the first day of classes in a new school, your first date, or the first day on a new job? You were probably anxious to know what would be expected of you. Appropriate behavior in those situations was important for you.

Children are confronted with many "firsts." What is appropriate behavior in response to the neighbor's new puppy? Your toddler may need guidance to gently touch his "first" new puppy.

What is appropriate behavior in response to a classmate who asks to copy Joey's homework before the teacher comes into the room? Your ten-year-old may need guidance to remain caring and yet firm in his response.

What is appropriate behavior in response to the gang's insistence on breaking speed limits? Your teenager may need your support in how to handle this first of many dilemmas between appropriate behavior as defined by society and as defined by peers.

On occasions, specific circumstances redefine appropriate behavior. Bedtime may be a definite routine in your household. Your preschooler has come to rely on a precise order of events at a particular time. When circumstances dictate a change in the routine, try to give children an explanation and advance notice whenever possible.

Life would be far simpler for parents and children if appropriate behavior could be easily defined and consistently maintained. The child is growing and maturing, the adults are responding to their own unique backgrounds, and circumstances are constantly changing. Parenting by grace challenges us to acknowledge each of these elements as we define, redefine, and effectively communicate our expectations regarding appropriate behavior.

Refer to the agree/disagree activity you completed at the beginning of this section. Make any changes you wish in light of new understandings.

Here is how I responded to the statements. 1—disagree. True, some behavior *is* a matter of moral absolutes and does not depend upon parental expectations, but all behavior is certainly not a matter of moral absolutes. 2—disagree. 3—agree. All cultural expectations are not wrong but some cultural expectations have created some artificial differences. 4—agree. 5—agree.

Affirming Appropriate Behavior

Before we discuss what to do about problem behavior, we need to be clear about what kind of behavior we want from our children.

What kind of behavior do we want from preschool Johnny in the grocery store? Often our only expectation is that a child not cause trouble. He may have a pretty good idea of what *not* to do, but he is not at all sure of what he is supposed to do. Tell Johnny what you want from him, and praise him and affirm him when he meets or exceeds your expectations.

Mom might talk with Johnny before they go to the grocery. "Johnny, there are lots of things in the store that you would like to have. Some of them are not good for you, and I want you to eat things that will help you grow. I want you to decide what kind of cereal you would like to have—corn flakes or oat circles. When we have put all the things on my list in the cart, you may pick a treat. You can decide which kind of fruit you would like to have."

Then while shopping, Johnny and Mom can play a guessing game. Look at the label and see if you can guess what's inside. Let Johnny take a can of green beans off the shelf, and tell him how much you appreciate his help.

These activities give Johnny some good learning opportunities. They also provide Mom with the chance to tell Johnny what a big help he is and how much she enjoys shopping with him. They also provide an opportunity to reinforce Johnny's appropriate behavior.

Dinnertime has become chaotic in the Smith household. Six-year-old Missy, tired from the day, stays seated only for a moment, then runs off, comes back for another bit, and runs off again. Her twenty-month-old brother copies her behavior. Both children often end up running around the table and generally creating havoc. Mrs. Smith says over and over, "Sit down and eat, Missy!" She threatens to throw Missy's food in the garbage if she doesn't come back and eat it. Missy returns for a few moments and then is up and running again.

Mr. and Mrs. Smith decide that the time has come for a little more discipline at dinner. Let's look ahead three days to the same suppertime scene. Missy has come to the table for a few bites. Mrs. Smith says, "Look at how well Missy is sitting at the table. I am so proud of you, Missy. I love having my family sitting at the table together. I'm glad we are a family." Missy beams and pipes in, "I'm glad we're a family, too. Guess what we did today, Daddy?" A few moments later she gets up to pick up a toy. Mrs. Smith says to Missy's little brother, Tommy, "And look how big you are, Tommy! I'm so proud of you for sitting at the table!" Missy pops back in her seat and asks, "What's for dessert?"

Is this discipline? When we think about discipline, we think about how God has shown us that discipline by grace builds us up. Punishment that tears down the spirit of a child has no place in a Christian home. Of course, we sometimes have to correct our children. But the basic tool of discipline by grace is affirmation and encouragement. Mrs. Smith encouraged Missy to do what she wanted her to do. Not only did Missy end up feeling better about herself, but her parents succeeded in getting the change they wanted.

The spiritual development of children depends on parents who affirm appropriate behavior. Child development research shows that children who are praised and encouraged by their parents for doing what is expected learn self-control and self-discipline. Children who are punished for breaking rules instead of praised and encouraged for keeping rules do not learn self-discipline. These children depend more on others to enforce the rules. Children who receive punishment as the main source of discipline don't resist temptation as well as children who are encouraged and praised by their parents. So when we encourage right action by our children, we help them grow spiritually. We teach them self-discipline.

Discipline differs from punishment in its time orientation. Punishment focuses on the past. Discipline focuses on the future. Proverbs 19:18 says, "Discipline your son, for in that there is hope" (NIV). We want our children to grow in grace. We do not aim to punish them for what they have done in the past. The question we must ask ourselves when disciplining a child is "What will she learn?" not "What does she deserve?"

When Missy's mother decided to praise six-year-old Missy for sitting at the table, she taught Missy something— "Mother likes for me to sit at the table. She loves me and my family. Sitting at the table makes everybody feel good." How do you think this affirmation by Mrs. Smith could help Missy grow spiritually? _____

_____

If Missy's mother had thrown her supper in the garbage and sent her to bed, Missy would have learned something else: "When I don't do what Mother says, she gets very angry. When I'm angry, it's OK to get even by doing something to the person who made me angry. I had better sit at the table the next time if I don't want to be hungry." How do you think this action by Mrs. Smith would have affected Missy's spiritual development?

_____

_____

At times, of course, we do need to discipline our children in negative ways. Don't get the idea that discipline by grace means all praise and no rebuke. Children need to feel the consequences of what they do. If Missy keeps bobbing in and out of her seat, she may need to be sent to her room until she is ready to sit at the table with the rest of her family.

In lesson 6 we will look at some guidelines for dis-

couraging unacceptable behavior. But a parent's major tool is encouragement and affirmation.

One activity in each lesson has been for you to affirm or celebrate a behavior or action by your child. What

results have you noticed? _____

_____

_____

Methods of Reinforcing Appropriate Behavior

1. *Scout ahead.*

We should look ahead for opportunities in which our child has a good chance to behave properly. A parent is asking for trouble if she takes her five-year-old son to a fancy restaurant where it takes an hour to get the food and another hour to dine. Sitting in a fast-food restaurant booth provides a better place for that parent to reinforce the child's appropriate behavior. There, she can use statement such as, "It is so much fun to go out to eat with you. I'm glad you're my son."

What is one example of where you failed to "scout

ahead"? _____

_____

2. *Match the reinforcement to the child's age.*

When we praise our children and reinforce that behavior, we need to be conscious of their ages. Telling sixteen-year-old David that we are proud of him for sitting at the supper table with us would be ridiculous, but it fits six-year-old Missy.

What is one example you have observed where parents failed to match the reinforcement to the child's

age? _____

_____

3. *Reinforce appropriate expressions of feelings.*

Twelve-month-old Babs just sent the carefully built block castle of her eight-year-old brother flying in all directions. Matt responds by yelling, "Stop that! I hate you. You're always messing up everything!" Mom yells from the kitchen, "I don't want to hear you talk like that to your sister!

What would be a better response for the mother to

make in this situation? _____

_____

Sometimes we can help a child express his feelings. Mom might say, "You're very angry at her for hitting your blocks. Use your words and tell me about it." Often we expect children to be more controlled than we are!

4. *Reinforce your child's unique personality.*

Each child differs from every other. When parenting by grace, parents don't try to treat all children the same. They find ways their children are different. Then they encourage their children to develop these strengths and gifts.

In the group study of lesson 1 you completed a "Personality Profile" on your child(ren). Review that worksheet.

Think of ways your child is unique. Write a summary description of the uniqueness of your child. If you have more than one child, use separate sheets of paper.

_____

_____

_____

5. *Reinforce the specific behavior of the child.*

All of us know that compliments which are specific mean more. If you want your children to continue doing something, tell them just what it is you like. Missy's mother said, "I'm proud of you for sitting in your seat." That is much more affirming and helpful to Missy than, "You're such a good girl." Being specific helps children to do better in the future. Missy will probably sit in her chair even longer the next night at supper.

Make a list of specific appropriate actions or behavior of your child that you would like to reinforce.

_____

_____

_____

Think of ways you can reinforce these specific actions.

6. *Reinforce appropriate behavior by validating positive experiences.*

If the long-term goal of discipline is self-discipline, we do not want children to become overly dependent on praise from parents or other authority figures.

We want the child to value his own positive experiences. On occasions, you might say: "You must feel good about the neat lettering on your science project." You have confirmed or validated the value of his careful work. Your teenager is reinforced in his effort to become more inner directed.

Children who learn to rely on external praise will be more vulnerable to inappropriate suggestions or directives from others. An internal sense of control has long-term benefits.

What are some positive experiences your child has had recently? _____

_____

Think of ways you can validate or confirm these positive experiences.

7. *Reinforce appropriate behavior by accentuating the positive.*

As you greet your child at the end of the day in the day care center, do you smile and say, "You must have had fun painting with blue paint," or do you say, "When will you ever learn to keep your clothes clean?"

When your ten-year-old straightens his room, do you note with pride the careful arrangement of books, or do you predict, "You'll never be able to find your socks at the back of that drawer"?

After your teenager brings a friend home to meet the family, do you say, "She was so thoughtful and considerate of Amy. Does she have a younger sister?" or do you say, "Where does she buy her clothes? I thought she was going to a costume party"? Remember your response to your child's friends is an indirect response to your child.

What are some examples of how you accentuate the positive in affirming and guiding your child?_____

_____

_____

_____

What is an example of how you have violated this principle or method? _____

_____

8. *Reinforce appropriate behavior by loving unconditionally.*

We affirm and reinforce our children specifically to build them up and help them grow, but we love them unconditionally.

What are some ways that parents communicate to children that their love is conditional?

_____

_____

_____

What are some ways that parents communicate to children that their love is unconditional? _____

_____

_____

Underline the eight methods of reinforcing appropriate behavior in the preceding section. Analyze each method and circle what you consider to be the key word or words in the statement.

The key words I selected are listed below (but not in the order they appear in the text). Using them as hints, write each method.

age _____

_____

personality _____

_____

love _____

_____

scout _____

_____

specific _____

_____

positive _____

_____

child's experiences _____

feelings _____

_____

Check your work to make sure you understand the methods. Read each method again and think of how you could explain the method to another parent.

Checkpoint
1. Define in your own words *appropriate behavior*.

_____

_____

2. Appropriate behavior depends upon what three factors?

a. _____ b. _____ c. _____

3. State at least five methods of reinforcing appropriate behavior in your child.

a. _____

b. _____

c. _____

d. _____

e. _____

Check your work with the answers in the "Summary."

Reflection and Application
1. Identify and reinforce at least three appropriate behaviors in each of your children this week. Complete the chart (use separate sheets of paper for more than one child).

Child's appropriate behavior	How I reinforced the behavior

2. You prepared for lesson 5 by identifying some traits or strengths in your child that you would like to affirm or encourage. Review these strengths on page 51. In the margin beside each one list some specific actions you can take to affirm and encourage those traits or strengths in your child. Implement these actions with your child this week.

3. Spend a few minutes reflecting on the following questions. (No written response is necessary.)

• How well did your parents affirm your appropriate behavior when you were growing up?

• What do you think are some problems or difficulties in affirming a child's appropriate behavior?

• What is the biggest problem you have in affirming your child's appropriate behavior?

• Who, in your opinion, does an exceptionally good job in affirming their children's appropriate behavior?

• Are you consistent as a parent in defining what is appropriate behavior for your child?

• Why is it often easier to accentuate the negative rather than the positive?

• How would you explain the statement, "Whereas punishment focuses on the past, discipline focuses on the future"?

4. You are now halfway through Parenting by Grace. This would be a good place to stop and review all of your work to this point. Spend a few minutes reviewing lessons 1-5. Read the summary for each lesson.

• Is the course helpful? Is it practical?
• Are you putting the principles and concepts into practice with your child(ren)?
• What are the overall results in your own life as a par-

ent up to this point in your study?

• What overall results have you noticed in your child(ren)?
• What problems or difficulties, if any, are you experiencing in completing all of the activities?
• Do you need to make any changes in your study habits during the last half of the course?

5. Evaluate yourself on how well you practice the methods of affirming appropriate behavior.

| Method | I practice this method | | | | |
	Seldom			Consistently	
a. I scout ahead.	1	2	3	4	5
b. I match the reinforcement to the child's age.	1	2	3	4	5
c. I reinforce appropriate expressions of feelings.	1	2	3	4	5
d. I reinforce my child's unique personality.	1	2	3	4	5
e. I reinforce the specific behavior of my child.	1	2	3	4	5
f. I validate my child's positive experiences.	1	2	3	4	5
g. I emphasize the positive.	1	2	3	4	5
h. I love my child unconditionally.	1	2	3	4	5

6. You may wish to talk with your children and explain to them the nature of this course and how it is helping you as a parent. Ask them what changes or improvements they have noticed in you.

Summary

1. Appropriate behavior is behavior considered suitable and acceptable by the parent.
2. Appropriate behavior depends on the child, the parent, and the situation.
3. Methods of reinforcing appropriate behavior:
• Scout ahead.
• Match the reinforcement to the child's age.
• Reinforce appropriate expressions of feelings.
• Reinforce your child's unique personality.
• Reinforce the specific behavior of the child.
• Reinforce appropriate behavior by validating the child's positive experiences.
• Reinforce appropriate behavior by accentuating the positive.
• Reinforce appropriate behavior by loving unconditionally.

Looking Ahead

Lesson 6 focuses on what to do about problem behavior. Complete the following activity as you prepare for the lesson.

What is a recent example of your child's inappropriate behavior or misbehavior? _____

_____

What was your response to your child? _____

_____

What do you think your child learned from your response? _____

_____

Can you think of a more appropriate response you could have made? If so, what? _____

_____

_____

Lesson 6
Discipline Finds Alternatives to Replace Inappropriate Behavior

Looking Back
Lesson 5 focused on the significance of affirming appropriate behavior. The three factors that determine appropriate behavior were identified and appropriate behavior was defined. The lesson centered on eight practical methods of affirming appropriate behavior. Turn to the "Summary" on page 59 and review the lesson. You prepared for lesson 6 by analyzing a recent example of misbehavior by your child.

Overview
This lesson is the reverse side of the coin from lesson 5. What do you do when the child misbehaves? How do you handle inappropriate behavior? Inappropriate behavior is defined, and two consequences of a parent's failing to respond properly to inappropriate behavior are pointed out. Nine methods for dealing with inappropriate behavior are examined.

Learning Goals
After completing this lesson, you should have a better understanding of how to handle inappropriate behavior.

You will be able to—
• define inappropriate behavior;
• state two results or consequences of a parent's focusing on inappropriate behavior but failing to handle it properly;

• state at least five methods for dealing with inappropriate behavior;
• analyze at least one behavioral pattern with your child where the behavior is inappropriate and outline plans for dealing with the situation;
• implement at least three of the methods for dealing with inappropriate behavior.

Inappropriate Behavior
Defining *inappropriate behavior* is easy when you recall the definition of *appropriate behavior*. Write your

definition of *inappropriate behavior.*_____

_____

_____

Inappropriate behavior may be defined as unsuitable, unacceptable, or failing to meet certain expectations. If your child's actions and attitudes are unacceptable to you, then you consider the behavior as inappropriate.

Inappropriate behavior of children can easily claim our time and attention. If a struggle between children's misbehavior and ineffective or inappropriate parental responses dominates the family relationship, undesirable results or side effects occur:

1. *The atmosphere in the home may become negative and punitive in nature.*

Children feel angry, guilty, discouraged, or rebellious. They may do what we want them to do—at least while we are watching. But researchers have found that the more parents focus on children's inappropriate behavior, the more children will obey when they are being watched and disobey when they think they can get away with it. On the other hand, children who are affirmed more often do what they are told, even when no one is watching.

The more negative and punitive the parent becomes the more distance develops between parent and child. This distance makes it harder for the parent to encourage the child. In their book *Living with Children* (Research Press, 1971), Gerald Patterson and Elizabeth Gullion suggest that the parent's attention is not as important to the child whose behavior is discouraged frequently as it is to the child who is encouraged.

Home sometimes becomes a no-man's land of uneasy peace between taking periodic shots at one another. Parents and children would rather avoid one another than risk an angry interchange. They "can't talk" to one another.

Indicate on the scale below your emphasis in discipline, both before you began this course and at the present. Circle a number.

Before I Began This Course

I focused primarily on dealing with inappropriate behavior.	I focused primarily on affirming appropriate behavior.

1   2   3   4   5   6   7

At the Present

I focus primarily on dealing with inappropriate behavior.	I focus primarily on affirming appropriate behavior.

1   2   3   4   5   6   7

Characterize the atmosphere of your home by placing an *X* at the appropriate place on each line below.
The Atmosphere of My Home

Negative _____ Positive
Distant _____ Close
Hurried _____ Relaxed
Punitive _____ Affirming
Fussy _____ Peaceful
Tense _____ Happy

If you have a teenager, ask him to write a paragraph describing the atmosphere in your home. Compare the description by your teenager with your rating above. What perceptions does your teenager have about the atmosphere of your home? How does your perception compare with your teenager's? (No written response is necessary.)

If you could change one thing about the atmosphere

of your home, what would it be? _____

_____

_____

Fifteen-year-old Bruce has the habit of leaving his dirty clothes in the bathroom floor. Mom responds by fussing, "You are an absolute slob. Why can't you learn to pick up after yourself? Honestly, I'm not your slave!"

Bruce responds with "Oh, Ma!" and halfheartedly picks up his clothes. Mom feels better—he has done what she has asked. He feels some relief; at least she has stopped nagging. He does better at picking up his clothes for a few days, and she doesn't say anything more about it. Then he slips and leaves his clothes from one end of the bathroom to the other. Mom explodes, "I can't believe you! You never listen to me! When will you ever learn?" Bruce grumbles something under his breath about how he can't wait until he's old enough to get away from a nagging mother, slams into the bathroom, and picks up the clothes.

Analyze the situation above. Reflect on the following questions. (No written response is necessary.)
• What does Bruce learn from the discipline?
• What effect does the discipline have on Bruce?
• What effect does the discipline have on Mom?
• What do you think will be the long-term effects of the discipline on Bruce?
• How would you characterize the atmosphere of this home?

Summarize how Mom could have handled the situa-

tion more effectively._____

_____

_____

Let's look back at what happened with Bruce and Mom. Mom learned that fussing works, at least in the short term. When Bruce did what she wanted, she didn't say anything. After all, why rock the boat? The problem is, Bruce got no encouragement for being self-disciplined. When he lapsed, what happened? Of course, Mom fussed. Remember? She has learned that fussing works. Bruce again teaches Mom that fussing works—he picks up his clothes. What has Bruce learned? He has learned that Mom fusses at his mistakes but doesn't seem to notice when he does what he's asked. Mom is a pain in the neck. He can avoid her fussing by picking up his clothes, but we wonder if he will do that when he gets off to a college dorm. Probably not, because the only reason he picks up his clothes is to quiet Mom. He has not learned to feel good about himself as a self-disciplined and orderly person. He looks forward to getting out on his own to do as he pleases. And this is not what his mother wants to teach him at all.

2. *Children become more aggressive.*

When we fail to help children find suitable alternatives to inappropriate behavior, they become more physically and verbally aggressive than children who are disciplined principally through encouragement. Abused children often show this in therapy by destroying toys, especially dolls that represent family members. Most abusing parents were abused as children. They did not learn whatever their parents were trying to teach them by beating them—they learned to beat others. Abused children show this tendency to be aggressive most vividly, but all children who are discouraged often are more likely to be aggressive.

The teenager Bruce, whom we just talked about, slammed into the bathroom as his mother fussed at him. Watch your child the next time you punish her. Often children who are afraid to attack a parent will hit or yell at a younger brother or sister or the family pet, slam a door, tear up a doll, or do something else to express frustration and aggression. Although often necessary, one of the most serious problems with physical punishment is that it teaches children to hit others when they don't like what they do. It makes children more aggressive.

Do you recall a way that you expressed frustration

and aggression while growing up? _____

_____

What is one way your child has expressed frustration

and aggression? _____

_____

Of course, children on occasion need to feel the consequences of their problem behavior. The Bible teaches that this may be in the form of physical punishment (see Prov. 10:13). We are stressing, though, that the balance of discipline needs to be on the side of reinforcement, praise, reward, and unconditional love. Discipline which discourages problem behavior must be placed in the context of encouraging right action and attitude. Children need to feel our unconditional love, even when we physically punish them or are angry or disappointed, even when we try to discourage problem behavior (see Eph. 4).

Problem behavior presents a continuing challenge to most parents. Parents are tempted to seek simple solutions to complex problem behavior. If the simple solution seems to work (even momentarily), we are likely to continue certain practices even though negative side effects may develop.

For example, threatening or bribing a child may

appear to stop him from teasing his little sister. What are the negative side effects? He remains dependent on someone to reward or punish him. He has failed to learn more appropriate, satisfying ways to interact with his little sister or with you. He has missed an opportunity to grow to a new level of maturity and independence.

What is inappropriate behavior? _____

_____

What are two results or consequences of a parent's focusing on inappropriate behavior and failing to deal with it properly?

a. _____

b. _____

Methods for Dealing with Inappropriate Behavior

Parenting by grace calls for us to help our children learn from their mistakes. We want to scout ahead, to help them avoid those situations which usually lead to misbehavior. We also want to affirm them and guide them along the way. But when they do break the rules and act in unacceptable ways, we want to discourage that behavior from occurring again. Our actions as parents must focus on how we can give them what they deserve. The following guidelines will help us deal with inappropriate behavior. They will help us replace inappropriate behavior with alternatives.

1. *Identify and emphasize appropriate behavior for your child.*

If you want your child to stop doing something, tell her what she can do instead that is appropriate behavior. You might say: "You may not kick your friend when you are angry. You may kick your soccer ball as hard as you like. You may tell your friend why you are angry."

Each time we discipline our children by discouraging their behavior in one way, we need to provide encouragement to them to act in another way.

Let's think for a moment about Missy, whom we met in lesson 5. Before her parents began encouraging her to sit at the table, all they did was discourage her from getting up and running around. They made lots of comments about that. In fact, when she finally would sit down for a few moments, they would almost hold their breaths and say nothing—enjoying the peace.

But what happened? Missy only got their attention when she ran around. They were not encouraging her to act in a more disciplined way. When they began to praise her and talk to her when she was sitting in her chair—along with sending her to her room to "calm down" when she got up—they were discouraging the problem behavior and encouraging her to act in the ways they wanted. The two kinds of discipline work best when they are used together.

You discipline your seven- and eight-year-old daughters for fighting by sending them to their rooms to calm down. But then you watch; and when you find them later in the day helping one another, you reinforce their appropriate behavior. "I am so proud of how you two can work together," you tell them. "You are really growing up when you work out your differences so well."

Refer to the inappropriate behavior of your child that you identified in lesson 2 (page 33). What are two substitute actions your child could take that would be appropriate behavior?

_____

_____

2. *State the boundaries.*

Tell your children what the boundaries and rules are. Don't wait until Susie has gone across the street by herself to tell her that she must stay in her own yard. Tell her when she first goes outside to play. Before you take the children grocery shopping, explain just what they can and can't ask for. Then stick to it!

Tell your child just what you expect from him before the company comes for dinner. This lets him know what he can and cannot do.

Tell your teenager just what you expect from her. Discuss with your daughter what she is to do if the crowd she is with starts using drugs or driving too fast.

List several boundaries your parents identified for you.

_____

_____

_____

Did you have a problem as a child accepting the

boundaries? _____

How do you feel about those boundaries?

_____

_____

List several boundaries you have identified for your

child. _____

_____

_____

Spend a few minutes thinking about these boundaries. Consider the following questions. (No written response is necessary.)
- Do you have too many?
- Are they fair and reasonable?
- Are they too tight?

- Do they give your child room to grow?
- What is the purpose of each one?
- Have you communicated clearly the boundaries to your child?
- Should any of them be changed?

What seems to be the general attitude and response of your child toward boundaries?

_____

_____

3. *Live by your own boundaries unless you've got a good reason for not doing so.*

Your children often turn out to look and act surprisingly a lot like you. Be sure that is what you want.

Don't expect from your children what you aren't willing to do. This is particularly important for elementary-age children. Rules are important to them. But this guideline really applies to all groups. The best example for our children is their parents. If children are allowed to watch only one hour of television in the evening, you'd better have a good reason for watching two hours yourself.

Show your children what you want by what you do. Don't buy junk food for yourself if you won't let your children have their own junk food.

Of course, children learn and understand that parents do some things that they can't do—drive a car, stay out late, cross the street to visit a neighbor, or climb up in the attic. But for the most part, the language we use, the food we eat, the activities that fill our time—all of these need to be within our own limits.

Share an example of how you have violated this

guideline. _____

_____

4. *Respect your children.*

Try to put yourself in their places and understand their side of things. After all, the goal of discipline is to help them grow and learn to act in more acceptable ways. We can't guide them if we don't understand why they did what they did. That may not mean that they are excused, but it is impossible to discipline by grace if you don't know why your children act the way they do.

A five-year-old burned a hole in the living room rug. He had taken the toaster from the kitchen to the living room and was holding a piece of paper over it when it caught on fire. He dropped the burning paper and burned the rug.

The father was furious. Before acting out of anger, though, he asked the little boy what he was doing. The child had seen an experiment in one of his library books in which lemon juice was used as "magic writing" on paper. When the paper was heated, the writing became visible.

He was trying to copy what he had seen. The father's response was different than it would have been if the child had continued to play with matches after he had been told not to play with them.

Have you ever changed the discipline you had planned after you understood your child's point of view and why he did what he did? If so, describe the incident.

_____

_____

5. *Fit your expectations to your child's age.*

Know what you can and cannot expect of your child, as we discussed in the stages of development in lesson 3. Do not punish a child for something she cannot yet understand.

A three-year-old walks out of the grocery store with a tiny car in his pocket. Dad doesn't discover it until they are in the car going home. He is furious with his son. "When we get home, you're getting a spanking. No son of mine is going to be a thief." What's wrong with this kind of discipline? A three-year-old has not learned yet that the store owns the car and it has to be paid for. He doesn't understand money or ownership yet.

What would be a better response for Dad to make

to his three-year-old? _____

_____

_____

Sometimes we make mistakes on the other extreme, too. Children growing up so fast sometimes scares us. So we try to hold them back. Our boundaries are too tight and we don't give them room to grow.

Refer to the boundaries you listed on page 63. Does each boundary fit your child's age? (No written response is necessary.)

6. *Label the behavior, not the child.*

Whether you are praising your child or pointing out a problem, you need to be specific. Use an arrow, not a shotgun—you'll make your point better. The shotgun approach is made up of words such as "You're such a good boy/bad boy" or "You're beautiful/sloppy." The arrow approach is made up of words such as "I am so proud of how you've studied to bring up your grades"; "I want you to study more next term"; "You did a beautiful job of combing your hair. Your part is so straight!"; or "You haven't combed your hair this morning. Go comb it while I fix your breakfast."

Think of a time recently when you violated this guideline. Describe the incident.

_____

7. *Be selective in response to children's misbehavior.*

The more parents remove privileges, rebuke their children verbally, or spank them, the less effective they become as parents. The more you try to discourage behavior, the less likely you are to get what you want from your child. To say it another way, the more often you use one method of punishment, the harder you have to work to get it to work. If you only spank your child, you have to spank that child harder and harder to make an impression. The normally softspoken parent who yells is going to be heard. The parent who yells all the time will be ignored.

Read again the guideline above. Rewrite it in your

own words. _____

_____

8. *Be swift and sure.*

Research has shown that the sooner behavior is followed by either reinforcement (praise or reward) or punishment (discipline which discourages problem behavior), the more likely the behavior is to change. That means you have to plan ahead. Know how you want to discipline your children so you don't have to decide when you're angry or frustrated. Then do it.

Rewrite the method above in your own words.

_____

_____

9. *Make discipline understandable.*

Natural consequences allow our children to experience the results of their behavior. For example, Mom tells seven-year-old Joe, "If you don't settle down and go to sleep, you will be tired tomorrow."

When parents need something more immediate than natural consequences, logical consequences are useful. Sometimes the natural consequences are too long in coming, but we can speed them up. For example, we may not want our child to wait to find out if she doesn't study, she won't have the grades to get into college. We choose a logical consequence instead. "If you don't get your homework done before supper, you can't watch television."

The least effective means of discouraging behavior is contrived consequences. These are not related to problem behavior. They are simply the only way a parent can think of at the moment to stop a behavior. Spanking is one of many examples of a contrived consequence. By itself, it does not lead to self-discipline and growth, although it may stop a problem behavior for the moment. We help our children grow up in the real world by helping them deal with natural consequences of behavior. Discipline needs to be understandable.

Describe an incident where you have used natural consequences as discipline.

_____

_____

Describe an incident where you have used logical consequences as discipline._____

_____

_____

Describe an incident where you have used contrived consequences as discipline. _____

_____

_____

Underline the nine methods for dealing with inappropriate behavior in the preceding section. Analyzie each method and circle what you consider to be the key word or words in the statement.

The key words I selected are listed below (but not in the order they appear in the text).

respect _____

_____

boundaries _____

_____

understandable _____

_____

age _____

_____

swift _____

_____

appropriate behavior _____

_____

live by your own _____

_____

selective _____

_____

label behavior _____

_____

Check your work to be sure you understand the methods. Read each method again and think of how you could explain the method to another parent.

Checkpoint

1. Define *inappropriate behavior.*

_____

_____

2. State two results or consequences of a parent's focusing on inappropriate behavior but failing to handle it properly.

a. _____

b. _____

3. State at least five methods for dealing with inappropriate behavior.

a. _____

b. _____

c. _____

d. _____

e. _____

Check your work with the answers in the "Summary."

Reflection and Application

1. Select an inappropriate behavior of your child that you have not already referred to in this course. Select a misbehavior with which you are currently having a problem.

Describe the inappropriate behavior.

_____

_____

Analyze the inappropriate behavior. Consider the following questions. (No written response is necessary.)

• What appears to be the cause of the behavior?

• What discipline have you used in the past with this behavior?

• What have been the results of the discipline?

• Why do you think the behavior keeps recurring?

• Which of the methods of dealing with inappropriate behavior have you failed to implement?

• What are some suitable alternatives to the misbehavior?

Now outline plans for dealing with the inappropriate behavior. Be specific in describing what you intend to do. _____

_____

_____

_____

_____

_____

_____

2. Implement at least three of the methods for dealing with inappropriate behavior this week. Complete the chart.

Child's misbehavior	How I handled the situation	Apparent results

3. Evaluate yourself on how well you use the methods for dealing with inappropriate behavior. Score your report card with a letter grade beside each method.
A—Excellent; *B*—Good; *C*—Fair; *D*—Poor; *F*—Failed

_____ 1. I identify and emphasize appropriate behavior for my child.

_____ 2. I state the boundaries.

_____ 3. I live by my own boundaries unless there is a good reason for not doing so.

_____ 4. I respect my child and try to understand his side of things.

_____ 5. My expectations fit my child's age.

_____ 6. I am specific and label the behavior, and not my child.

_____ 7. I am selective in response to my child's misbehavior and do not overuse one method of punishment.

_____ 8. I am swift and sure in following behavior with reinforcement or punishment.

_____ 9. I make the discipline understandable to my child.

Spend a few minutes thinking of ways you can improve in any area where your grade is *C* or lower.

4. Don't forget that the main emphasis in parenting by grace is affirming appropriate behavior rather than focusing on misbehavior. Continue your practice of reinforcing appropriate behavior. Complete the chart.

Child's appropriate behavior	How I reinforced the behavior

5. Spend a few minutes reflecting on the following questions. (No written response is necessary.)

• How did your parents deal with your misbehavior when you were growing up?

• Did your parents' methods work?

• Would you say that your parents knew how to parent by grace?

• What is the most vivid memory you have of being disciplined for misbehavior?

• What is the biggest problem you face as a parent in dealing with inappropriate behavior?

• Are you consistent in dealing with inappropriate behavior?

• Which method of dealing with inappropriate behavior is most difficult for you to practice?

• Do you think the child should be involved and have a part in setting his boundaries?

Summary

1. Inappropriate behavior is behavior considered unsuitable and unacceptable by the parent.

2. Results or consequences of a parent's focusing on inappropriate behavior and failing to handle it properly:

   • Negative and punitive home atmosphere
   • Children become more aggressive.

3. Nine methods for dealing with inappropriate behavior:

   • Identify and emphasize appropriate behavior for your child.
   • State the boundaries.
   • Live by your own boundaries unless you have a good reason for not doing so.
   • Respect your children.
   • Fit your expectations to your child's age.
   • Label the behavior, not the child.

   • Be selective in response to children's misbehavior.
   • Be swift and sure.
   • Make discipline understandable.

Looking Ahead

Lesson 7 is on "Seizing the Teachable Moment." The lesson will help you in teaching your child. Complete the following activities as you prepare for the lesson.

1. Identify and describe the most influential teacher (other than your parents) in your life.

_____

_____

_____

2. Write your definition of *teachable moment.*_____

_____

_____

Unit Four

Applying Grace to Your Parenting

Lesson 7
Seizing the Teachable Moment

Looking Back

Lesson 6 focused on how to handle inappropriate behavior. The heart of the lesson was nine practical methods or guidelines for dealing with inappropriate behavior. Turn to the "Summary" on page 67 and review the lesson.

Overview

This lesson shifts to a different emphasis—how to use the teachable moment with your child. *Teachable moment* is defined and your responsibility to teach your child is emphasized. Six guidelines for recognizing and using teachable moments are explained. You will be involved in responding to different situations involving teachable moments.

Learning Goals

After completing this lesson, you should have a better understanding of how to use the teachable moment in the parenting process.

You will be able to—
• define *teachable moment*;
• describe your responsibility as a teacher in parenting;
• state at least four guidelines for recognizing and using teachable moments;
• structure an opportunity for a teachable moment with your child;
• evaluate a teachable moment experience with your child.

Teachable Moments

Mark each statement *T* (true) or *F* (false).

_____ 1. Teachable moments come spontaneously; they cannot be created.

_____ 2. Teenagers are too old to respond to teachable moments.

_____ 3. Teachable moments are the daily opportunities to discipline and guide our children toward Christian maturity.

_____ 4. The church has the primary responsibility to teach spiritual and moral values to children.

_____ 5. Children think in concrete images.

_____ 6. Parents should never lecture to their children.

_____ 7. Parents should discuss issues with their children rather than lecture to them.

_____ 8. Children express their thoughts and feelings better in words than in actions.

_____ 9. Parents should refrain from saying "I don't know" to their children.

_____ 10. Parents should always be honest with their children.

_____ 11. *Discipline* means "to teach."

_____ 12. A parent should not initiate a discussion with his child on the decision to follow Jesus.

Check your work as you study this lesson.

Sharon loves working with her daddy in the garden. As they poke the seeds into the warm earth, cover them, and water them, they talk about God making the seeds and sending the rain and sun to help them grow. In sharing with her daddy, his listening to her questions and talking with her, Susan feels the love of God which nurtures her own spiritual growth.

This moment will probably have a greater influence in Sharon's life than the actual words they say to one another. What we say is not as important as the actions that back up or undergird what we say. Values and beliefs are more easily caught than taught.

The Bible speaks in several places about children growing up to follow the example (not necessarily the teaching) of their parents. Read the following Scripture passages and complete the chart.

Scripture	Child	Parent(s)	Example of parent (good or bad)
1 Kings 15: 25-26			
1 Kings 22: 51-52			
2 Chronicles 17: 1-4			
2 Chronicles 26: 1-5			
2 Timothy 1: 3-5			

Sharon's daddy had a choice. The rows would have been straighter and the garden planted more quickly so he could settle down with a glass of iced tea and the paper if he had sent Sharon to play with someone else. He chose instead to talk with her and let her help him with his work. By choosing to include her, he taught her that she matters to him, that she is important. He recognized a teachable moment.

Parents are often described as children's first and foremost teachers. The tutorial method of one-on-one instruction has consistently proved superior to every other method of teaching. As parents, we are confronted with an incomparable opportunity and responsibility to share Christian values and ideals with our children.

Teachable moments are the daily opportunities to discipline and guide our children toward Christian maturity. In fact, the word discipline comes from the Latin word *disceo* which means "to teach." If parents understand discipline as primarily a matter of snuffing out misbehavior, they become smoke detectors rather than teachers.

Underline the definition of *teachable moment* in the paragraph above. Compare it with the definition you wrote in lesson 6 (page 67).

Describe two recent teachable moments you have

experienced with your child. _____

_____

_____

Parents' Responsibility to Teach

We parents can use the special moments that come in everyday life to teach our children spiritual and moral values. This may mean pausing in the middle of a frantic rush to get out the front door in the morning—or pausing when we have things on our mind other than a discussion with our children. Rarely do these moments come when our emotional circuits are not overloaded, making it difficult to concentrate on our children's needs. Nevertheless, these moments make lasting impressions on our children.

Read Deuteronomy 6:4-9. Hebrew parents were responsible for teaching God's laws to their children on these everyday occasions:

a. _____

b. _____

c. _____

d. _____
Rewrite verse 7 in your own words.

_____

_____

_____

_____

_____

State in your own words what verse 7 means to you.

_____

_____

Guidelines for Recognizing and Using Teachable Moments

How can we as parents recognize and use these teachable moments to help our children grow spiritually? There are several guidelines we can use.

1. _Know your child._

The first guideline is to know your child. See the world from her point of view. Children are not miniature adults; they have limits that we are often not aware of.

For example, preschoolers live in the here and now; they do not understand the passage of time well. Mother can become frustrated with Johnny, who asks every few moments, "Can I get up now, Mommy?" She may respond, "I said you have to lie quietly for thirty minutes for your rest. Now don't ask me again!" Of course, Johnny has no idea how long a period of thirty minutes is.

We think our children understand many of the words we use. But they are far beyond most children's capabilities. Words such as sin, salvation, justice, grace, and temptation are difficult for a child. They are abstract; children think in concrete images. For example, a child reciting the Lord's Prayer was overheard to say, "And lead us not into Penn Station." Many times when parents think children are stubborn or disobedient, children really do not understand what is being asked of them.

Describe an experience where your child did not understand the words you were using.

_____

_____

Lesson 3 provides some detailed guidelines of what children the age of your child can be expected to understand. Remember, though, that these are just guidelines. They will not fit any child exactly. They may give you some ideas to explore in your own understanding of your child, but they are not enough by themselves. You have to know your own child.

What are some tips or pointers you have found helpful in getting to know and understand your child better?

_____

_____

2. _Discuss; don't lecture._

The second guideline is to discuss issues with your child instead of giving a lecture. Earlier we talked about answering children's questions. Often, however, children do not put words to their concerns. Especially preschool children, but even some adolescents, express their thoughts and feelings better in actions than in words we can hear.

What is the difference between a lecture and discussion? _____

_____

Why do you think many parents find it easier to lecture than to discuss issues with their child? _____

_____

Draw an arrow between parent and child to show the flow of communication when a lecture is used.

parent   **child**

Now draw an arrow or arrows between parent and child to show the flow of communication when discussion is used.

parent   **child**

Why is discussion between parent and child more important than a lecture from parent to child?

_____

Parents struggle with discussion. Many find it easier to answer the question and go on to other things. But by listening, by putting yourself in your child's shoes and seeing the world her way, you have communicated that her questions are important, that she is a person worth receiving attention.

Listen, reflect, watch. Take time to see your child. What does his posture tell you and what does his behavior show? A stomachache can be too much candy, trouble at school, or apprehension over conflicts in the home. Ask questions; then count to twenty before either demanding an answer or asking another question. A discussion is give-and-take between two or more people. Respect your children enough to enter into a discussion with them.

3. _Be honest._

Answer a child's questions as honestly as you can.

Don't be afraid to say, "I don't know." Children can accept and handle the truth better than the distrust and unbelief that come when parents tell them untruths or half-truths to protect them or make something easy for them.

Describe an incident where you told your child a half-truth. _____

_____

_____

Because we love our children, we want to protect them from hurt. But we must look at how God parents us. He does not promise an easy life, but He promises to be with us in the hard times.

In some situations, recognizing that the answer is not pleasant or easy—or that we do not know the answers—may be the only true answer.

4. *Be available in everyday events.*

Little things count. If you are available in everyday events, your child will know you are available in the "big" events.

If our children learn they can count on us to be there to change a messy diaper, repair a broken tricycle wheel, study spelling words, or attend football games, then they will trust us to be there when their world falls apart, hurts come, friends are fickle, and people disappoint them. If you do not take time to mend your child's broken toy, she will probably never come to you for help in mending a broken heart.

5. *Teach as you discipline.*

God requires us to discipline our children. We don't have an option as Christian parents about whether to discipline our children. Discipline means much more than punishment, though. *Discipline* means "to teach." Teach and discipline are synonymous in the Bible (Heb. 12:5-8). The goal of discipline by grace is to help our children grow spiritually and morally.

Particularly in response to misbehavior, we are often tempted to simply stop the misbehavior without recognizing the opportunity to teach.

6. *Create your own teachable moments.*

Special times like birthdays, holidays, family worship, storytelling, and family ministry projects help parents and children trust each other with thoughts and feelings. We do not have to wait for teachable moments to happen on their own. There are ways we create teachable moments in the lives of our children. These enrich our own lives, as well as the spiritual and moral dimensions of our children's lives.

How do you celebrate your child's birthday?

_____

How have you used holidays such as Thanksgiving and Christmas as special teaching moments with your children? _____

_____

_____

Gear your family worship and Bible study to a level of discussion that children can understand. Build on their actual experiences. Allow the Holy Spirit to work.

In all activities—everyday moments, family traditions, family worship, storytelling, and family ministry—we lead our children toward development of their own faith. The time often comes, however, when we want to discuss with our older children and adolescents the decision to follow Jesus. We have learned how to talk with our children along the way as we have taught them. This may be a life-changing discussion time, yet the same guidelines apply:

• We know our children and talk with them, not try to make them fit a formula.

• We listen and discuss, not lecture.

• We are honest, sharing what we know and what we don't know, helping them to ask questions instead of providing all the answers.

• We do not presume to know more than the Holy Spirit, pushing them before they are ready.

• We recognize that our child is God's child. God must move in his life, and we cannot control that or make it happen.

Our children are unique individuals; we can love them, share with them, talk with them, but they will go their own way. God planned it that way.

Underline the six guidelines for recognizing and using teachable moments. Study each one and circle what you consider to be a key word or words in the statement.

• The key words I selected are listed below (but not in the order they appear in the text). Using them as hints, write each guideline.

create _____

honest _____

teach _____

available _____

know _____

discuss _____

Check your work to make sure you understand the guidelines. Read each guideline again and think of how you would explain it to another parent.

Refer to the true-false statements on page 69. Check your work with the answers: 1. False. Teachable moments *do* come spontaneously many times, but they can also be created. 2. False. No person is too old to respond to a teachable moment. 3. True. 4. False. Parents have the primary responsibility to teach spiritual and moral values to children. 5. True. 6. False. This one was deliberately misleading. As a rule, parents should discuss issues with their children rather than lecture them. However, there can possibly be times when a lecture is in order. 7. True. 8. False. Actions speak louder than words when it comes to children expressing their thoughts. 9. False. There are many times when the only right answer a parent can give is "I don't know." 10. True. 11. True. 12. False. We should always be sensitive to the leading and working of the Holy Spirit and not rush ahead too quickly. However, we should be ready and willing to initiate a discussion when the time is right.

Responding to Teachable Moments

How would you handle the following potential teachable moment situations?

Situation 1

You've been working hard all day and you've just gotten a chance to sit down and relax. Your five-year-old comes to you with an old flashlight and says, "I can't make this work. What's wrong with it?" You look at it and say rather impatiently, "The batteries are dead." Your child says, "What's a battery? What makes it work? Why are they dead?"

How would you respond? _____

_____

Situation 2

Tomorrow is Saturday, your child's eleventh birthday. She comes bouncing into the room and says, "Tomorrow's my birthday. Let's do something special."

What would you do to make your child's birthday

special? _____

_____

Situation 3

You've been working hard all day and you've just gotten a chance to sit down and relax. Your teenager comes to you with an algebra book and a pencil and says, "I can't figure out this problem. Will you help me?"

How would you respond? _____

_____

Checkpoint

1. Define *teachable moment.*_____

_____

2. Describe your responsibility as a teacher in parenting. _____

_____

_____

3. State at least four guidelines for recognizing and using teachable moments.

a. _____

b. _____

c. _____

d. _____

Check your work with the answers in the "Summary."

Reflection and Application

1. Plan an activity you can use with your child this week that will create an atmosphere for a teachable moment. It might be a special storytime, a walk, a shopping trip, a meal out together, or some special occasion like a birthday or holiday. Follow through and do the activity.

2. If the above activity resulted in a teachable moment, evaluate the experience. If no teachable moment developed, then evaluate another teachable moment you have had with your child. Consider these questions. (No written response is necessary.)

• Was the teachable moment spontaneous or did you create an atmosphere for it to develop?

• What were the circumstances that led to the teachable moment?

• Which of the six guidelines did you use?

• What were the results of the teachable moment?

• What would you do differently if you could relive the teachable moment?

3. Give yourself another report card, this time on how well you use the guidelines for recognizing and using teachable moments. Use a letter grade (*A, B, C, D,* or *F*) beside each guideline.

_____ (1) I know and understand my child well.

_____ (2) I discuss issues with my child rather than lecture.

_____ (3) I am completely honest with my child in all matters.

_____ (4) I am available to my child in everyday events.

_____ (5) I use discipline as a teaching tool.

_____ (6) I work to create teachable moments with my child.

Spend a few minutes thinking of ways you can

improve in any area where your grade is *C* or lower.

4. Find in your Bible at least two situations where Jesus made use of a teachable moment. Record your findings.

Scripture	Description of teachable moment	Results

5. Keep a record this week of the amount of time you spend with your child(ren) each day. Use the chart. Record the amount of time in the spaces below the days.

Child's name	Sun.	Mon.	Tue.	Wed.	Thu.	Fri.	Sat.

6. Be alert to watch for teachable moments with your child(ren) this week. Keep a record of them on the chart.

Child's name	Description of teachable moment	Results of teachable moment

7. Continue your practice of reinforcing appropriate behavior. Complete the chart.

Child's appropriate behavior	How I reinforced the behavior

8. Remember that the emphasis in parenting by grace is on affirming appropriate behavior. However, there are times when inappropriate behavior must be dealt with. Keep a record this week of any misbehavior you handled. Use the chart.

Child's misbehavior	How I handled the situation	Apparent results

9. Reflect on the following questions. (No written response is necessary.)
- What are some teachable moments you remember from your childhood?
- Were your parents available to you in everyday events?
- Near the end of lesson 6, you identified the most influential teacher (other than your parents) in your life. How did this person make use of teachable moments?
- Where do your children receive most of their spir-

itual and moral teaching—in your church or in your home?

• What is one action you can take to be a better teacher with your children?

• How can you become more sensitive to spontaneous teaching moments with your child?

• Do you agree or disagree with the following statement? Why? "Values and beliefs are more easily caught than taught."

• What are some spiritual and moral lessons you are teaching your children by example?

• Do children *always* follow the example of their parents?

• What was a recent occasion when you responded to your child, "I don't know"?

• Do you find it difficult or easy to talk with your child about spiritual matters?

• If your ten-year-old child came to you and said, "I want to become a Christian," what would you do? How would you help your child?

Summary

1. A teachable moment is the daily opportunity to discipline and guide our children toward Christian maturity.

2. Parents are responsible for teaching their children through all the events and circum-

stances of everyday life.

Six guidelines for recognizing and using teachable moments:

• Know your child.
• Discuss; don't lecture.
• Be honest.
• Be available in everyday events.
• Teach as you discipline.
• Create your own teachable moments.

Looking Ahead

Lesson 8 is on "Teaching Through Example." The lesson will help you be a better model for your children. Complete the following activity as you prepare for the lesson.

Identify and describe one of the most influential models (other than your parents) in your life. (Do not select the teacher you chose in lesson 6.) _____

_____

_____

_____

Lesson 8
Teaching Through Example

Looking Back
Lesson 7 dealt with the teachable moment, that special time when we have the opportunity to guide our children in spiritual growth. The lesson centered around six guidelines for recognizing and using the teachable moments. Turn to the "Summary" on page 75 and review the lesson.

Overview
This lesson continues the emphasis on teaching—this time on the importance of modeling and how to teach through example. Modeling is defined and the strong effect of the example set by the parent is emphasized. Six guidelines for teaching through example are explained. The potential and limitations of parental models are pointed out. Then the influence of other models on children is examined.

Learning Goals
After completing this lesson, you will have a better understanding of teaching through example.

You will be able to—

• define modeling as a parenting technique;
• state at least four guidelines for teaching through example;
• identify two of your limitations as a model;
• name the three primary models in children's lives;
• take at least two specific actions to become a better model in your parenting.

Parents as Models
Look up *model* in your dictionary and select the definition that you think best fits this lesson. Write it below.

_____

_____

_____

A mother overheard her five-year-old daughter talking to her two-year-old brother as they were both coloring at the kitchen table. "That's really good coloring, John. You used very pretty colors. Why, it's a rainbow!" Although John had scribbled all over the paper in random fashion, his sister had searched for a way to make him feel good about the work he had done. Even though he had had no intention of making a rainbow, he beamed back at her a smile that said, "I'm glad you like my picture."

No one instructed the five-year-old, "Be nice to your brother. Find something nice to say." Where did she learn to talk to him this way?

Of course, we answer that she learned from her parents when they made her feel good about her own work. Her words were an echo of what she had heard from her parents on other occasions.

One dictionary defines *model* as "an example to be emulated." The word *emulate* means "to strive to equal or excel, especially through imitation." This gives an awesome definition of modeling as a parenting technique; namely, *parents are examples that their children strive to equal or excel, especially through imitation.* This is true, good or bad, regardless of whether we want it to be so.

It should not surprise us that our own behavior teaches more powerfully than any other way of teaching. The Bible points out the importance of parents setting an example for their children.

Read again 1 Kings 15:25-26; 22:51-52; 2 Chronicles 17:1-4; 26:1-5; 2 Timothy 1:3-5. Review the chart you completed in lesson 7, page 70.

Summarize in your own words what these biblical passages infer about how we are to parent.

All of these passages illustrate that what we say is not as important as the actions that back up or undergird what we are saying. Psychological research with children underlines this biblical truth. Values and beliefs are more easily caught than taught. Parents who do not live Christian values will not pass those values on to their children.

Research on the moral development of children has found that the example set by a parent is a more powerful teacher of moral judgment than anything he might do to a child by way of encouraging or rewarding him or punishing him. If we ranked the ways we can help children grow spiritually and morally, modeling by parents would be the most powerful method; encouraging the child through praise or reward would be next; and punishing the child would be least effective.

Now write your own definition of modeling as a parenting technique. _____

Guidelines for Teaching Through Example

1. *Know what your values are and live by them.*

Values are those activities, beliefs, or involvements to which we give our time, money, and energy.

A working mother who spends two hours in the late afternoon fixing a hot dinner to take to the family of a sick friend demonstrates the value of friends. A father who puts down his book to read to his preschooler shows what he values.

We continually choose what we will invest ourselves in, what is most important to us. Each time we make such a choice, we teach our children. This kind of teaching sticks with us over the years, even though we may not be aware of it.

For example, many busy families constantly struggle to make time for one meal together each day where members can share with one another. Why? No one ever said to them, "You must always have at least one meal during the day to talk with one another." But Mom and Dad remember this time in their own childhood, and they learned.

As Christians, our desire is to love God, others, and ourselves. Paul describes these values in Galatians 5:22-23. All of us act out these values in different ways, but they form the core of our faith. We teach love when we show love; we teach forgiveness when we are forgiving; and we teach trust when we are trustworthy.

We sing the hymn, "Trust and obey, for there's no other way to be happy in Jesus, but to trust and obey" (John H. Sammis, "When We Walk with the Lord"). We want our children to trust Jesus. But they learn to trust Jesus by first learning to trust us. Our actions as parents have to be such that when our children trust us and are obedient, they find it is for their own good, not just to get them out of our way for the moment.

The choices we make about how we use our time, energy, and money teach our children about our values and about what is most important to us.

Read the following list of values. Beside each one write a number to represent how important this value is to you. A *3* means it's very important to you; a *2* stands for important; a *1* represents not so important. Blanks are left for you to fill in with values that are important to you but which aren't on the list.

_____ kindness	_____ peer acceptance
_____ honesty	_____ peace
_____ responsibility	_____ security
_____ self-motivation	_____ excitement
_____ prestige	_____ challenge
_____ material wealth	_____ dependability
_____ physical fitness	_____ church commitment
_____ family life	_____ career success
_____ trustworthiness	_____ friendship
_____ self-control	_____ patience

Now examine your ranking and circle every value assigned a *3*. From this list select the top five priority values in your life. List them below in order of priority, the most important value listed first.

_____

_____

_____

_____

Spend a few minutes reflecting on your values. Consider these questions (no written response necessary):

• What did you learn about your values from having to rank them in priority?

• Which of your highest values, if any, would you like to change?

• Are there any values which you don't want your child to imitate? Why?

• How does your list compare to Paul's list of the "fruit of the Spirit" (Gal. 5:22)?

For each of the concerns and activities on the following list which are applicable to an adult, compare your own behavior to the expectations you hold for your child.

Concern/Activity	Expectations for my child	My own behavior
Meals		
Homework		
Recreation/Exercise		
Watching television		
Church attendance		
Grades		
Household chores		
Sibling relations		
Money management		
Work		
Peer relations		
Driving the car		
Use of tobacco/ alcohol/drugs		

Are you playing by your own rules? Circle the concerns/activities where your own behavior is inconsistent with your expectations for your child.

State at least two actions you can take to discipline yourself and become a better model? _____

_____

_____

2. *Parent your child as God parents you.*

This concept has been referred to a number of times in this course. Exactly what does the image of God as a model parent mean? Summarize briefly in your own words how God parents us. _____

_____

_____

_____

Why did God choose us to help Him work out His purpose for His creation? Surely He could have done a much better job without our help. By including us in the work, however, by allowing us to minister, He teaches us how to love by His own love for us. That's parenting by grace.

We are to parent our children, then, as God parents us. The main understanding of God for our children is what they experience in the relationship with the powerful persons in their lives—parents.

3. *Treat other persons as gifts of God, unique and of great worth.*

We teach our children by how we treat other people in our lives. Other persons are gifts of God, unique and of great worth. We recognize their worth no matter who they are or how we are related to them. No one is an object to be used.

Examine how you relate to the waiter in the restaurant, the clerk in the store, the parking lot attendant, the custodian at your church. Do your children sense your respect for every person? Children learn attitudes, prejudice, love, and hate by watching, listening to, and imitating the ways their parents treat others.

4. *Listen to and understand your child.*

Ask your child what he thinks before telling him what you think. This encourages him to begin thinking for himself instead of assuming that someone else always has the right answer.

When our children ask questions, we need to listen and look for what answers they are really seeking, then do our best to fulfill their need.

The following questions are typical of the kinds of questions preschoolers ask. Write what you think may be the need behind the question. Then think of how you might respond to answer the spoken question and also to meet the unspoken need.

• "Mommy, would you be sad if I died?"

Unspoken need: _____
• "Daddy, are you coming back to get me?"

Unspoken need: _____
The following questions are typical of the kinds of questions elementary-children ask.

• "Daddy, what happenend to Grandpa after he died? Can he see us from heaven?"

Unspoken need: _____
• "Where do babies come from?"

Unspoken need: _____
The following questions are typical of the kinds of questions teenagers ask.

• "Why am I so ugly (fat, skinny, dumb, etc.)?"

Unspoken need: _____
• "Don't you trust me?"

Unspoken need: _____
5. *Involve yourself and your family in ministry events.*

Children learn by doing, whether it's math or ministry. We must show our children how to be loving, caring Christians by involving them in ministry.

Act out love for your neighbors in specific ways in which your children can be involved. This may be something as simple as fixing homemade cookies for a friend in the hospital and letting your child decorate the plate or make a card to go with it.

What is one ministry event you and your family can

do this week? _____
6. *Seek guidance and support in the fellowship of the church.*

We need all the help we can get! Within the church we can find support and guidance as we try to teach our children by example. Also, as we participate regularly in worship, the educational programs, and the ministries of our church, we provide a consistent example for our children.

Complete this statement: "My church helps me most

in my parenting by _____
Underline the six guidelines for teaching through example. Study each one and circle what you consider to be a key word or words in each guideline.

The key words I selected are listed below (but not in the order they appear in the text). Using them as hints, write each guideline.

ministry _____

listen _____

church _____

God _____

other persons _____

values _____
Check your work to make sure you understand the guidelines. Read each guideline again and think of how you would explain it to another person.

Limitations and Dreams of Parental Models

Without a doubt, parents are the most significant influence in most children's lives. The potential for parents to shape children's attitudes and behavior translates into an awesome responsibility and privilege.

Most of us are quick to recognize that we are not perfect. We have our limitations as models for children. From an early age, children sense inconsistencies in our lives. When we are annoyed or disappointed or upset and try to suggest to children that everything is OK, they know better!

Since we are not able to serve as a perfect model, there are times we make mistakes and need to apologize to our children. We are able to say: "I'm so sorry. I made a mistake. I should have given you time to explain why you were late and missed the school bus this afternoon."

Because we are not perfect models, there are also

times when we help our children understand that we are still developing as Christians. We acknowledge the challenge of loving our neighbors as ourselves. The opportunity to grow together through Bible study, family worship, and ministry activities can prove most rewarding to parents and children.

Identify two limitations or weaknesses of yourself as a parental model.

_____

_____

What kind of parental model would you like to become? Every parent dreams about the future. Spend a few minutes with some of your dreams. Complete the following activity.

• What dreams for the future do you have for your

child(ren)? _____

_____

• Are you parenting as you thought you would before

your child was born? _____

_____

• What are you teaching through example? _____

_____

• What talents or skills do you think God may have

given your child(ren)? _____

• What are you doing to encourage these talents?

_____

• Pray about your child(ren). Talk with God about your dreams. Ask Him to guide you and your child(ren) toward the future.

Other Models for Children

We are reminded regularly that our children are confronted with other models in their lives. Observers of modern families suggest that children's lives are primarily influenced by parents, television, and their peer group.

Circle in the paragraph above the three primary models in children's lives.

Television

Mass media models are of particular concern to many parents and professionals. The powerful influence of television commercials can be seen as young children repeat slogans and hold out for favorite advertised items in the grocery store. Older children may assume that there are easy solutions for complex problems. After all, television families successfully resolve major issues within a half-hour program.

Teens may have difficulty staying with a challenging reading assignment. Fact and fiction on television are presented in an easy to absorb manner. Less is expected of the viewer than is expected of the reader. The life-styles of mass media models often present values that conflict with Christian parents' values.

How do parents effectively respond to the model of television in children's lives? Note the following list of possible parental approaches. Identify one or two advantages and disadvantages for each approach.

Parental Response to Television		
Parental approach	**Advantages**	**Disadvantages**
Ban television from the home.		
Limit time spent viewing television.		
Review and select suitable programs (with child's opinion considered).		
Avoid viewing television during meals.		
View selected programs with the child(ren).		
Encourage children to develop critical viewing.		
Set a good example. (How much time do you spend watching television? Which programs do you view?)		
Provide other experiences for children's learning and recreation activities (visit the library; plant a tree; bake bread; do an errand for a neighbor).		

Peer Groups

Peer groups seem to serve as a powerful model, both positive and negative, for behavior and attitudes from an early age. Obviously children may pick up bad habits from their friends and playmates. However, the emotional and social development of children can also be enhanced and supported by friends. Elementary-age children may be confronted with a host of conflicting models. Just as each child's family is unique, so values, attitudes, and behavior of each child may vary from your expectations.

Acknowledge the differences and similarities between your child's family and his friends' families. Help your child to sort through and affirm those positive, healthy, Christian characteristics he discovers in his friends.

The early teen years are often seen as the time when young people are most vulnerable to negative peer pressure. Affirm your teen's desires to be an accepted member of her group. A sense of belonging is apparently critical to healthy personality development. Help your teenager to develop strong, healthy friendships by being a good friend to others.

If you have a teenager, does she feel comfortable bringing her friends home with her? _____

Other Models

All parents are indebted to wise, thoughtful, caring adults who help rear healthy children in a troubled society. Single parents or parents in blended families may be particularly sensitive to the contributions of significant persons in their children's lives. The complexity of missing models, multiple models, and/or conflicting models challenges our best parenting skills. Recognize your own limitations. Acknowledge the necessity of assistance in parenting. Visit with your minister, physician, your child's teacher or a good friend as you seek help in a particular situation.

Take time to express your appreciation to—
• your child's classroom teacher who reinforced his positive self-concept;
• the neighbor who took time to help your daughter fill the bird feeder;
• the Sunday School teacher who visited your child's home;
• the friend who stood by your teenager;
• the pediatrician who expresses his interest in your child's total well being;
• the piano instructor who affirms your child's talent and sets high standards for her performance;
• the grandparent who includes your child in his visits to the elderly.

Checkpoint

1. Define *modeling* as a parenting technique.

2. State at least four guidelines for teaching through example.

a. _____

b. _____

c. _____

d. _____

3. Identify two of your limitations as a model.

a. _____

b. _____

4. Name the three primary models in children's lives.

a. _____ b. _____ c. _____

5. State two specific actions you can take to become a better model in your parenting.

a. _____

b. _____

Check your work with the answers in the "Summary."

Reflection and Application

1. Plan to initiate the two specific actions you identified above that will help you become a better model.

2. Involve your family this week in the ministry event you identified on page 79.

3. It's time for another report card. Use a letter grade (A, B, C, D, F) beside each guideline to indicate how well you use that principle.

_____ a. I know what my values are and I live by them.

_____ b. I do my best to parent my child as God parents me.

_____ c. I treat other persons as gifts of God, unique and of great worth.

_____ d. I listen to and understand my child.

_____ e. My family is involved regularly in ministry projects to others.

_____ f. I seek guidance and support in the fellowship of my church.

Spend a few minutes thinking of ways you can improve in any area where your grade is *C* or lower.

4. Continue to watch for teachable moments with your children this week. Keep a record of them on the chart at the top of the next page.

Child's name	Description of teachable moment	Results of teachable moment

5. Continue your practice of reinforcing appropriate behavior. Complete the chart.

Child's appropriate behavior	How I reinforced the behavior

6. Reflect on the following questions. (No written response is necessary.)

• What kind of models were your parents for your life?

• What is one important lesson you learned through the example of your parents?

• What is an example where your words and your actions were in conflict and did not match?

• Are you thoroughly committed to living by your values?

• What is one area where your own behavior is inconsistent with your expectations for your child?

• Do you show partiality or prejudice toward certain persons or groups?

• Why do you think children often have an unspoken need behind the questions they ask?

• Do you agree or disagree with the following statement? Why? "Television is a negative influence on children."

• Are you acquainted with all of your child's close friends?

Summary

1. Modeling as a parenting technique means that parents are examples that their children strive to imitate and equal.

2. Six guidelines for teaching through example:

• Know what your values are and live by them.

• Parent your child as God parents you.

• Treat other persons as gifts of God, unique and of great worth.

• Listen to and understand your child.

• Involve yourself and your family in ministry events.

• Seek guidance and support in the fellowship of the church.

3. Parents have limitations as models.

4. The three primary models in children's lives are parents, television, and peer groups.

Looking Ahead

"Experiencing and Celebrating Family" is the focus of lesson 9. The lesson introduces a new term, *Home Lifetime,* and explains how this special time can strengthen and enrich your family. Complete the following activity as you prepare for the lesson.

Recall the family celebrations and special events of your childhood.

• What were some of them? _____

_____

• What made them special to you? _____

_____

_____

Unit Five

Sustaining Grace in Your Parenting

Lesson 9
Experiencing and Celebrating Family

Looking Back

Lesson 8 focused on the most powerful method of all for helping children grow spiritually and morally—the method of modeling and teaching through example. The lesson centered around six guidelines for teaching through example. Turn to the "Summary" on page 82 and review the lesson.

Overview

This lesson deals with a family time called *Home Lifetime*. A brief overview of the family life cycle is presented to show the need for a family time together. *Home Lifetime* is described, including the five elements that compose it. The benefits of family *Home Lifetime* for both children and parents are pointed out. Nine practical guidelines for planning and participating in family *Home Lifetime* are given.

Learning Goals

After completing this lesson, you should have a better understanding of how to experience and celebrate family.

You will be able to—
• list at least three needs of your family members that can be met through a family time;
• describe *Home Lifetime*, including its five elements;
• list at least five benefits of *Home Lifetime*;

• state at least four guidelines for planning and participating in *Home Lifetime*;
• analyze your own family times;
• commit to begin *Home Lifetime* and plan to conduct at least four sessions.

Family Needs

The task of parenting needs to be understood in relation to the developmental needs of the child. A knowledge of these stages can aid parents in meeting the needs of their children as they grow. By being aware of both the children's and their own needs at any particular stage, parents can better fulfill this task.

The parenting task begins at the time an adult becomes responsible for a dependent child. The job of parenting continues throughout the lifespan but is continually redefined. For example, parenting preschoolers, teenagers, and median adult children all require different skills. Even role reversal may occur during the senior adult stage of parenting.

Underline the needs of children at the various life stages as you read the following overview of the family life cycle.

The basic task of the first year of life is the development of a sense of trust. Toddlers and preschoolers begin to develop a healthy sense of autonomy by being able to make simple choices within limits. As a child enters school, his self-image depends more and more on persons outside the home. He begins to discuss and develop his own gifts and interests.

The teen years provide an opportunity for youth to integrate their physical and intellectual endowments and their spiritual gifts. Parents need to provide teens opportunities to develop responsibility and thereby gain self-confidence.

Parenting does not stop when the child reaches adulthood, although a type of ambiguity between parent-child and adult-adult roles develops. Parents need to remain advocates and resource persons. They continue to model throughout the lifespan.

List several typical needs of family members at various life stages.

_____   _____

_____   _____

How can a family time help to meet these needs?

_____

_____

The family life cycle is a graphic reminder of our responsibility to parent by grace at each stage of development. Spending time together as a family is an important part of parenting by grace.

Preschoolers want and need to spend time with their families. "But wait," you might say, "I spend hours with my preschooler every day, meeting his needs, watching him, providing for him, playing with him." That's true. That's part of the parents' role. But how much time does your entire family spend together working on a common goal?

Children want and need to spend time with their families. In addition to school activities, many children are involved in church activities, Boy or Girl Scouts, music lessons, and sports. Children need the security and comfort of time spent working and playing as a family to give stability to their lives.

Teenagers want and need to spend time with their families. It is probably the last thing the typical adolescent would admit to wanting or needing. But during these crucial, crisis-filled, busy years, teenagers need to know that there will be times when they can return to the safety of their family for comfort, sympathy, and encouragement.

As family members grow and mature, new tasks and opportunities emerge. How can families work together to support and promote Christian development of each member? Will a conscious commitment to a specific family time make any real difference in the lives of children and parents? Obviously the answer depends in great part on the nature of the family time.

Spend a few minutes analyzing the family times in your home. Consider the following questions. (No written response is necessary.)

- What are the family times in your home?
- Does your entire family usually have one or two meals together each day? Is mealtime rushed or is it a happy time for sharing and being together?
- Do you have family worship or devotions in your home? If so, how often? Are all family members present? Do family members look forward to this time or is it a bedtime ritual?
- How do you celebrate special events like holidays or birthdays?
- Is your family regularly involved in recreational activities together?

The Family Home Lifetime

Home Lifetime is the term used to designate a weekly period when the family spends quality time together on some common project or goal. The focus is on being together and celebrating family.

The key elements of a family *Home Lifetime* include evaluation, celebration, recreation, anticipation, and preparation.

1. *Evaluation*

Think of your family *Home Lifetime* as an opportunity to identify strengths as well as areas needing improvement in your family life. Invite all family members to share their perspectives of the previous week.

Begin on a positive note. You might say, "Let's think about the best part of last week. Jason, you seemed really to enjoy inviting Daniel to spend the night with you." Depending on Jason's age, encourage him to describe the fun of sleeping on the floor in the den.

Listen for an opportunity to ask, "How can we make cleaning up the den easier the next time you have a guest?" Affirm Jason's suggestion to serve popcorn on TV trays.

Certainly effective parenting often requires an immediate response to children's behavior. Waiting until the next scheduled family time may be neither feasible nor practical. However, a time together offers the opportunity to reflect and evaluate the impact of a specific happening.

You might say to your teenager: "I'm glad we have this chance to talk with you about your English assignment. Do we need to schedule a time for you to visit the city library? Are the government documents an essential part of your paper?"

Honest evaluation means that we recognize the areas of difficulty in family life. Perhaps we need to discuss the challenge of everyone getting up and leaving the house early each weekday morning. Will packing lunches and choosing clothes the preceding evening help? Who can take a shower and shampoo at night instead of morning? Can homework consistently be placed near the back door?

Remember to contribute to the evaluation of family life the previous week. Express your gratitude for the cooperation of family members in rescheduling dinner because of your having to work late. Suggest that you are going to prepare a few casseroles for the freezer. In the future, these one-dish meals can help the family meals stay on schedule.

Evaluate your family's time together last week. Complete the chart.

Positive features	Areas needing improvement

2. Celebration

Celebrations are most often associated with special events such as birthdays and holidays. Help children understand that family *Home Lifetime* is an opportunity to identify individual moments worthy of celebration. The positive, optimistic, Christian approach recognizes the biblical soundness of praise and celebration.

As a result of thoughtful evaluation, children are able to share those times of joy. While sharing grief diminishes the grief, sharing a joy enhances the joy.

When Carla shares her passing grade in algebra, expressions of delight can come from each member of the family. As Mom describes a new and challenging assignment at work, family members celebrate her accomplishment and offer words of encouragement.

Creative forms of celebration include worship and praise to God for the honoree, handwritten notes of congratulations, a favorite dessert, a chance to sleep late on Saturday morning, or tickets to the concert or theater.

Conclude your celebration with simple sentence prayers from each family member. Invite the honoree to select a favorite Bible verse to recite or read.

What is one recent accomplishment or event in your child's life that is worthy of celebration?

_____

What is a creative way your family could celebrate

that accomplishment? _____

_____

3. Recreation

The value of time away from the routine of housework, work outside the home, or school is widely recognized. Professionals often "prescribe" some form of recreation as a way to reduce stress and prevent burnout.

Families need to cooperatively pursue a form of family recreation which can meet the needs of children and parents. A young family with preschoolers may find a trip to a nearby park genuinely refreshing. While Dad and the children feed the ducks near the lake, Mom relaxes in the shade and reads her favorite magazine.

After the older children's soccer game, perhaps the entire family will enjoy an inexpensive treat at a fast-food restaurant.

Teenagers who are developing their photography skills may look forward to a fall hike in a local wooded area. A picnic or cookout may conclude a lovely afternoon with family members.

A quiet evening at home may be recreational as family members play a board game or arrange family snapshots in an album or try a new cookie recipe. Simple refreshments allow young children to assist in preparation and serving.

What are some recreational activities that your entire

family enjoys? _____

_____

4. Anticipation

Looking forward to the next few days or week can accomplish at least two important things for families.

First, families can anticipate and begin preparation to meet challenging situations. If the calendar reveals a conflict between a dental appointment for Mom and piano lessons for Sarah, there is time to reschedule or seek assistance from Grandpa or the weekly car-pool driver.

If weekend guests are expected, family members can share household chores so that guests are welcomed and not resented. Knowing in advance that you will need to give up your bedroom or share the closet makes the giving easier. Della may choose to put away games that her four-year-old cousin would find frustrating or confusing.

Second, families can also anticipate with pleasure the events of the next few days or week. Half the fun of a scheduled weekend trip, grandparents coming to visit, or a birthday party is the planning and anticipation.

Anticipate trying a new recipe, playing a favorite game, visiting an old family friend, shopping for the "perfect" gift, or baby-sitting for a new neighbor. Anticipation shared in a family *Home Lifetime* can enhance the experience.

What is something in the immediate future your family

can anticipate? _____

_____

5. Preparation

Finally, as family members evaluate, celebrate, recreate, and anticipate, they are preparing for the following week. As a result of time spent together focusing on areas of need as well as areas worthy of celebration, each member of the family should be better prepared to learn and grow from new opportunities in the days and weeks ahead.

Describe briefly in your own words *Home Lifetime*, including its five elements._____

_____

_____

_____

_____

Benefits of Family Home Lifetime

1. Positive time spent working and playing together as a family can help child(ren)—
• grow in self-esteem as he is accepted and affirmed within the family;
• be encouraged to discover and develop interests and abilities;
• accept and communicate feelings within an understanding family environment;
• learn how to relate to others by interacting with siblings, parents, and grandparents;
• be treated as someone special making a unique contribution to the family;
• appreciate the importance of working and playing together as a family;
• begin to understand the world around him;
• become aware of opportunities to minister to others within and outside of the family;
• build a better understanding of God through the values gained from a loving family.

2. Positive time spent working and playing together as a family can help parents—
• love and affirm each child;
• recognize and encourage each child's developing interests and abilities;
• guide children in appropriate expressions of feelings within an understanding family environment;
• reinforce appropriate behavior of children;
• offer alternatives to replace inappropriate behavior of children;
• recognize and use teachable moments;
• teach through example;
• become aware of opportunities to minister to others within and outside the family.

List several ways you believe your own family would benefit from *Home Lifetime.*

Guidelines for Family Home Lifetime

Here are nine practical tips on planning and participating in *Home Lifetime*:

1. Keep activities short and simple.
2. Schedule the family time at your child(ren)'s prime time. No one will enjoy the time if someone is tired, hungry, or fussy.
3. Make sure all family members are available.
4. Plan a snack you know your child(ren) will enjoy.
5. Maintain an atmosphere of encouragement and support. Your child(ren) will try new activities if you believe they can.
6. Encourage each family member to contribute in his or her own way. If a preschooler becomes frustrated by a picture that doesn't look right or an item that won't work, ask, "What could we do to help you with this problem?" If your teen seems bored, ask, "What could we do to make this more fun?"
7. Do not compare work. Praise and admire each child's contribution on its own merits.
8. Encourage your child(ren) to work at their own pace. Adjust the level of difficulty for the age of the child involved.
9. Collect any specific materials needed for the session (e.g., crayons and paper or tempera paint).

Home Life magazine has a regular feature called "Home Lifetime" which contains suggestions and resource material for implementing this family together time. Some suggestions for *Home Lifetime* are:
• Play board games and serve refreshments.
• Prepare a dress-up dinner, using the best dishes, favorite foods, dress-up clothes, and best manners.
• Attend a sports event, play, or movie as a family and then talk about feelings and thoughts it brought up.
• Plan a ministry project as a family to a needy family in your community. Prepare a meal and make arrangements through your church or a community service organization for continued help.
• Take turns sharing your favorite Bible passages and telling why they are meaningful to you.
• Plan special celebrations for holiday times, such as a family Easter sunrise service, a Fourth of July picnic, a Thanksgiving ministry project, or caroling in your neighborhood on Christmas eve.

List several activities your family would enjoy doing

together. _____

_____

_____

Checkpoint

1. Describe briefly *Home Lifetime*, including its five elements. _____

_____

2. List five benefits of *Home Lifetime.*

a. _____

b. _____

c. _____

d. _____

e. _____

3. State four guidelines for planning and participating in *Home Lifetime.*

a. _____

b. _____

c. _____

d. _____

Check your work with the answers in the "Summary."

Reflection and Application

1. List three needs of your family members that you believe can be met through *Home Lifetime.*

a. _____

b. _____

c. _____

2. Spend more time analyzing your family times together. Refer again to the questions on page 85. Then write a paragraph describing your family times.

_____

_____

_____

_____

_____

_____

_____

3. Obtain a copy of *Home Life* magazine from your church. Read the "Home Lifetime" section. Outline plans for two family *Home Lifetime* sessions with your family. Use separate sheets of paper.

4. Arrange to get your family together to discuss *Home Lifetime.* Make this decision time a miniature *Home Lifetime* session itself by preparing some favorite refreshments. Celebrate an accomplishment by one family member. Explain *Home Lifetime* and involve your family in discussion.

Make a commitment as a family to participate in at least four sessions of *Home Lifetime.* Reproduce the following Family Contract Card and ask family members to prayerfully consider and sign it.

Family Contract Card

The members of the _____
family contract together—
• to recognize the uniqueness of every family member;
• to thank God for placing us together as a family;
• to spend time as a family working, sharing, and playing together.

Date: _____ Signed: _____

_____

_____

_____

_____

---

5. Outline plans for the four *Home Lifetime* sessions. Involve other family members in this planning. (Do not simply use the plans you outlined in number 3 above.)

Summary

1. Children have special needs at each stage of their development. Spending time together as a family can help to meet many of these needs.

2. *Home Lifetime* is a weekly period of family time spent on a common project or goal. The focus is on being together. The five elements of *Home Lifetime* are evaluation, celebration, recreation, anticipation, and preparation.

3. The benefits of *Home Lifetime* are many. *Home Lifetime* helps children—

• grow in self-esteem;
• be encouraged to discover and develop interests and abilities;
• accept and communicate feelings;
• learn how to relate to others;
• be treated as someone special making a unique contribution to the family;
• appreciate the importance of working and playing together as a family;
• begin to understand the world about them;
• become aware of opportunities to minister.

Home Lifetime helps parents—
• love and affirm each child;
• recognize and encourage each child's developing interests and abilities;
• guide children in appropriate expressions of feelings;
• reinforce appropriate behavior;
• offer alternatives to replace inappropriate behavior;
• recognize and use teachable moments;
• teach through example;
• become aware of opportunities to minister.

4. Guidelines for planning and participating in *Home Lifetime*:
• Keep activities short and simple.
• Schedule the family time at your child(ren)'s prime time.
• Make sure all family members are available.
• Plan a good snack.
• Maintain an atmosphere of encouragment and support.
• Encourage each family member to contribute in his or her own way.
• Do not compare work.
• Encourage your child(ren) to work at their own pace.
• Collect materials needed for the session.

5. *Home Life* magazine has a regular feature called "Home Lifetime" which carries suggestions and resource materials for implementing *Home Lifetime.*

Looking Ahead

Lesson 10 is on "Parents: Sharing and Supporting." It is a "Where do we go from here?" type session. This particular Parenting by Grace course is almost over, but parenting by grace never stops! The session will help you as you continue to parent by grace in the months and years to come. Complete the following activities as you prepare for the lesson.

1. Reflect on the commitment you made in the introductory session to study, prepare for, and participate in this course.

2. Reflect on your study during lessons 1-9.

Lesson 10

Parents: Sharing and Supporting

Looking Back

Lesson 9 stressed the importance of a regular family time together. *Home Lifetime* was introduced, along with its benefits. Practical guidelines for planning and implementing *Home Lifetime* were shared. Turn to the "Summary" on page 88 and review the lesson.

Overview

This concluding lesson focuses on a parent support group. The benefits of a parent support group are identified, and resources for the group are spotlighted. Attention is given to single-parent and blended families. A review and self-evaluation measures your learning over the entire course. Closure is brought with a challenge to participate in a parent support group for at least two months.

Learning Goals

After completing this lesson, you should have a better understanding of the importance and value of parents sharing with and supporting one another.

You will be able to—

• state four benefits of a parent support group;

• identify two unique problems single-parent and blended families sometimes encounter;

• name at least three periodicals that provide resource material for parent support groups;

• make a commitment to participate in a parent support group for at least two months, meeting monthly.

Benefits of a Parent Support Group

For the third Saturday night in a row, John stormed to his room in obvious fury and disappointment, saying, "All the other kids watch it. I wish I had somebody else for my parents!"

His parents, George and Ruth, had refused to let him watch a television show known for its violence and destruction of property. They thought they had made the right decision, but now they were having doubts. They felt sorry that he felt left out of something that was important to his friends.

George said, "Well, I'm tired of this. I think I'll just find out if all the other kids do watch it!" He called the parents of two of John's ten-year-old friends at church. Both of the other parents said, "Well, we don't really like our son to watch that stuff, but it seems like all the kids do."

After thinking about it further, George and Ruth decided to do something about this and other rules that John questioned because "all the other kids can." They called some of the other parents and invited them to a meeting on Sunday night after church. Over cake and coffee, they began to talk about questions they had.

Out of that meeting, the parents reached some group rules—about TV shows that they would and would not let their children watch and where the kids were allowed to sit during church (not on the back row where their parents could not see them). They also made plans to request that the church start a boys' basketball team that would give the children a good outlet for their energy.

The group never became a formal organization, but parents learned to talk to one another and share in their parenting decisions.

What are two or three ways you have received help from other parents by participating with them in this

course? _____

A parent support group is a group of parents who meet informally to discuss mutual concerns. Sharing with parents whose children are approximately the same developmental level is the most common arrangement of support groups. Parent support groups can also be arranged so that parents' discussion revolves around a particular issue, such as homework or mealtime. Groups can also be arranged so that parents with similar experiences share and support one another, such as single-parent and blended families or parents with special children.

There are many benefits of such a group. By participating in a parent support group, parents are better able to—

1. *Understand their child's behavior*
Parents of four-year-olds or fourteen-year-olds recognize common characteristics of the age group. They understand that many four-year-olds experiment with bad language. They understand that many fourteen-year-olds begin to question previously accepted family and church values.

When parents recognize that four-year-olds sometimes use inappropriate language because it insures them of parents' attention, parents think of creative ways to give their preschooler special attention. Understanding that fourteen-year-olds are exploring a variety of values because they are seeking to make a personal commitment, parents may help young teens study their faith.

What is one way other parents have helped you to

understand your child better? _____

2. *Explore parenting issues of particular concern*
Parents faced with toilet teaching, poor appetites at mealtime, lack of responsibility for household chores, poor study habits, or defiant teen behavior will welcome an opportunity to explore the issue with other parents. Invariably one parent can recall similar circumstances and offer words of encouragement. All

suggestions may not be equally suitable; parents have to discover their own way.

As parenting issues are explored, parents may recognize their limitations and agree to invite a minister, counselor, educator, or pediatrician to meet with them. The various professional representatives can often assist in their efforts to handle parenting issues.

The professional may offer parents new information, healthy attitudes, and/or specific techniques or skills essential to parenting by grace.

What is one parenting concern you would like to discuss with other parents? _____

3. *Practice recommended principles of parenting by grace*
Earlier in these sessions, we acknowledged that parenting is not easy. Particularly, parenting by grace is not easy. In addition to reading and reflective thinking, the opportunity to practice principles of love and affirmation is essential to effective application to your family.

Within an accepting, warm, supportive atmosphere, parents can "try on" new ideas or role-play typical situations. Active participation enhances the learning potential for the members of the parent support group. For example, each parent in the parent support group can describe a typical scene in his family. Other parents can take turns responding in a positive, helpful approach.

Describe how parents in a group could actually practice their skills in creating a teachable moment.

4. *Understand the significance of their own behavior as parents*
In previous sessions you have been challenged to acknowledge that parents serve as children's first and foremost teachers. Parenting is teaching. Discipline is teaching.

Almost as surely as genetic influences are apparent in children, parental influences are apparent in children's behavior. For example, children learn values from their parents. For this reason, it's extremely important for parents to be aware of the values that govern their priorities, decisions, and behavior. They can be sure that these values will greatly influence their children. Parents can learn something of their values by sharing with other parents.

What is one thing you have learned from other parents about your own behavior as a parent? _____

5. *Identify personal areas of parenting that need strengthening while affirming strengths.*

Honest, open communication within a parent support group allows a parent to say, "Help!" Recognizing and acknowledging the need for assistance with a fretful infant, a fearful eight-year-old, or a determined teenager is the first step toward a healthy resolution.

Underline the five benefits of a parent support group in the preceding section.

Most parent support groups meet informally and do not have a structured study such as this course. Nevertheless, in a real sense you have been involved in a parent support group during this course. Evaluate the help you have received from your parent support group on the following scale.

My parent support group has helped me to:	Degree of help			
	Very little		A great deal	
1. Understand better my child's behavior	1 2	3	4	5
2. Explore and deal with parenting issues	1 2	3	4	5
3. Practice some of the principles of parenting by grace	1 2	3	4	5
4. Understand the significance of my behavior as a parent	1 2	3	4	5
5. Affirm areas of strength in my life and identify weaknesses	1 2	3	4	5

Single-Parent and Blended Families

Single-parent and blended families have unique challenges and opportunities that require the very best of parents. A parent support group is especially helpful to these families.

Analyze the following case study and make a list of suggestions of how the noncustodial parent could deal with the situation.

Courtney is six years old. Her mother and father have been divorced for four years. She lives with her mother, Kathryn. Her father, Jim, lives in another city about two hours away. The divorce settlement included a provision that Courtney would stay with her father for three weeks in the summer and a week at Christmas.

Kathryn and Jim's parenting styles are totally different. Although Kathryn is not a drunkard or promiscuous, she has little regard for spiritual values. She also tends to be overly critical of and impatient with Courtney. She doesn't take her to church or pray with her at home. As a result, Courtney is almost totally ignorant of God and the Bible. She also tends to be extremely timid and fearful of people. Jim is concerned that Courtney is not receiving the guidance she needs. But he feels powerless.

What can Jim accomplish with her in four weeks out of the year when her mother has her the other forty-eight weeks? _____

_____

_____

_____

How could a support group help Jim? _____

_____

_____

Many children today live in blended families—families composed of yours, mine, and (possibly) our kids. In this situation, a child could easily feel that she is not "as smart," "as pretty," or "as good" as her step- or half-siblings. Comparisons among children, intentional or not, can destroy their sense of unique worth.

If you are a member of a blended family, list characteristics of each child in your family that are unique to him. Emphasize the positive traits that make each child a special person. Use separate sheets of paper for your work.

Now think of specific ways you can show your child that you recognize and appreciate his uniqueness. Jot them down beside the traits you listed.

Elementary-age children understand rules. They do not understand when parents or other children can break the rules and they cannot. This is particularly difficult in blended families where each parent brings children from former marriages.

If at all possible, both parents involved should be consistent in making and enforcing rules. The key is communication between the two parents.

Consistency may be difficult for a single parent when the child visits with the other parent, and the other parent has different rules. If possible, it helps if Mom and Dad can lay down some common expectations for their children's behavior, even though they live in separate households.

If this is not possible, make clear to your children that although certain things are permissible with their other parent, the rules are different with you. Elementary-age children can understand and live with different expectations at school than they have at home.

Special occasions such as vacations, holidays, and birthdays often present a specific challenge for single-parent families and blended families. If yours is a single-parent or a blended family, what are some of the specific problems you have encountered in celebrating

special occasions? _____

_____

What are two unique problems single-parent and blended families sometimes encounter? Review the

preceding section to identify these. _____

_____

_____

If you are a single parent or a parent in a blended family, what is one unique problem you have faced?

_____

How did you resolve the problem? _____

_____

_____

_____

_____

Resources for Parent Groups

We have acknowledged from the earliest session that parenting by grace is not easy. Application of the principles of love, affirmation, discipline, and guidance require a prayerful approach committed to Christian development of each family member. Your parent group may find the following resources helpful.

Books

Empowered Parenting: Raising Kids in the Nurture and Instruction of the Lord by Robert J. Morgan (0-8054-9815-X) (LifeWay)

Building Strong Families Leader Kit (0-7673-2669-5) (LifeWay)

Peace in the Family Home Activity Book (0-7673-2584-2) (LifeWay)

Self-Control in the Family Home Activity Book (0-7673-3175-3) (LifeWay)

Truth Matters...For You and Tomorrow's Generation by Josh McDowell (0-8054-9834-6) (LifeWay)

Truth Matters Leader Guide (0-8054-9833-8) (LifeWay)

The Five Love Languages of Children Video Pak by Gary Chapman and Ross Campbell (0-7673-3899-5) (LifeWay)

The Five Love Languages of Children Parent Activity Guide (0-7673-3898-7) (LifeWay)

New Faces in the Frame: A Guide to Marriage and Parenting in the Blended Family by Dick Dunn (0-8054-9817-6) (LifeWay)

Shaping the Next Generation by David and Elaine Atchison (0-7673-3476-0) (LifeWay)

Shaping the Next Generation Leader Kit (0-7673-3484-1) (LifeWay)

Periodicals

ParentLife, a monthly magazine for parents of preschoolers and children, ages infant through eleven.

Living with Teenagers, a monthly magazine for parents of youth, ages twelve through seventeen.

HomeLife, a Christian family magazine designed to enrich Christian marriages and family life.

LifeWay Press has developed further material for parent enrichment. For more information write to your state convention Family Ministry program leader or to the Discipleship and Family Adult Department, LifeWay Christian Resources, 127 Ninth Avenue, North, MSN 151, Nashville, Tennessee 37234-0151.

Review the list of resources and place a check beside each periodical you receive regularly. Place a check beside each book you have read. Place a check beside each course you have studied.

Parenting Evaluation

Evaluation of your parenting style is a prerequisite to identification of areas that need strengthening. Review your parenting behavior and attitudes in response to the following situations.

Mealtime—trying to get help with preparation of a meal, cleaning up after one, the noise level during one, manners or the lack of manners, table conversation and topics of discussion.

Chores—who will do what and when, enforcement and assignment, settling disputes about chores.

School—support for teachers, encouragement of child, lack of interest, problems, grades, expectations of parents, teachers and students.

Homework—homework that is to be done, some that is left undone, some that is forgotten or lost, homework that is too hard or too easy.

Leisure—how it will be used, rules about it, time to be spent on it, money for it, prerequisites for it such as school work, chores, etc.

Money—getting it, spending it, and keeping it.

Friends—who they will be, where your child will go with them, how often your child will see them, bringing them home, how much time on the phone.

Church—going, not going, gripes about, activities.

Now evaluate your parenting behavior and attitudes on the following scale.

Area	My behavior and attitudes are questionable and need prayerful support.						My behavior and attitudes are outstanding.
Mealtime	1	2	3	4	5	6	7
Chores	1	2	3	4	5	6	7
School	1	2	3	4	5	6	7
Homework	1	2	3	4	5	6	7
Leisure	1	2	3	4	5	6	7
Money	1	2	3	4	5	6	7
Friends	1	2	3	4	5	6	7
Church	1	2	3	4	5	6	7

1. Identify the areas where you scored 5 or higher. Select your two strongest areas and list them below, with your strongest area listed first.

a. _____

b. _____

2. What is one way you can share your strengths in these areas with other parents? _____

_____

3. Identify the areas where you scored 3 or lower. Select your two weakest areas and list them below, with your weakest area first.

a. _____

b. _____

4. State two specific actions you can take to strengthen these areas of parenting.

a. _____

b. _____

Checkpoint

1. State four benefits of a parent support group.

a. _____

b. _____

c. _____

d. _____

2. Identify two unique problems sometimes encountered by single-parent and blended families.

a. _____

b. _____

3. Name three books or periodicals that provide resource material for parent groups.

a. _____

b. _____

c. _____

Check your work with the answers in the "Summary."

Reflection and Application

1. What are two areas of strength in your parenting?

a. _____

b. _____

2. What are two areas of weakness in your parenting?

a. _____

b. _____

3. Review and think about the benefits of a parent support group. Make a prayerful commitment to participate in a group for at least two months.

4. Spend some time reflecting on your involvement in this entire course.

a. Turn to page 13 and read again the purpose of Parenting by Grace. Evaluate how well you think you understand and practice the concepts presented in the course. Use a scale of 1 to 10 with 10 being outstanding and 1 being very weak. Place a number in each blank.

Concept	My understanding of this concept	My practice of this concept
1. The role of love and affirmation	_____	_____
2. The nature and use of discipline	_____	_____
3. The teachable moment	_____	_____
4. The role and importance of modeling	_____	_____
5. Family time together	_____	_____

b. What have you enjoyed most about the course? _____

c. What is one important truth that you believe God has taught you during this course? _____

_____

d. What is one thing you will resolve to do based on your study? _____

_____

Summary

1. Benefits of a parent support group:
- Helps parents to better understand their child's behavior
- Enables parents to explore parenting issues of particular concern
- Permits parents to practice recommended principles of parenting
- Helps parents to understand the significance of their own behaviors as parents
- Helps parents to identify strengths and weaknesses in their parenting

2. Single-parent and blended families sometimes encounter unique problems:
- Comparisons among children in a blended family
- Lack of consistency in making and enforcing rules for all children in a blended family
- Difficulty in celebrating special occasions such as vacations, holidays, and birthdays

3. The Discipleship and Family Development Division provides a number of resources to help parents. See page 96 for a listing of these books and periodicals.

4. Parents need to identify areas of strength and weakness in their parenting style. This is a prerequisite to improvement.

Conclusion

Congratulations again! Ten lessons ago we congratulated you for beginning Parenting by Grace, and now you have completed the course.

Parenting by Grace is more that a new phrase, another good idea, or even a Baptist program. It is a way of life, a lifestyle, a decision. Parenting by Grace works. It will work in your life, in your home, and with your children. With God's guidance you can love, affirm, discipline, and guide your children with the kind of grace He offers you.

Parenting by Grace is not a quick fix or a miracle cure. It is an attitude that comes when you accept God's gift of grace and pass along to your children.

Can you imagine a home in which the parents relate to their children in all circumstances with unconditional love and mercy—where parents and children are in a right relationship with God and their behavior is guided by the Holy Spirit? Sound too good to be true? It is God's model. It can be your home as you risk loving, affirming, disciplining, and guiding by God's grace.

Our prayer for you is that parenting by grace will become a way of life and that your parenting might be pleasing to God in every area.

Resources for Parent Enrichment

The following items are available by writing Customer Service Center, MSN 113; 127 Ninth Avenue, North; Nashville, TN 37234-0113; by calling toll free (800) 458-2772; by faxing (615) 251-5933; by ordering online at *www.lifeway.com;* by emailing *customerservice@lifeway.com;* or by visiting a LifeWay Christian Store.

Books

Empowered Parenting: Raising Kids in the Nurture and Instruction of the Lord by Robert J. Morgan (0-8054-9815-7) (LifeWay)

Building Strong Families by Bill Mitchell (0-8054-6370-4) (Broadman and Holman)

Building Strong Families Leader Kit (0-7673-2669-5) (LifeWay)

Peace in the Family Home Activity Book (0-7673-2584-2) (LifeWay)

Self-Control in the Family Home Activity Book (0-7673-3175-3) (LifeWay)

Truth Matters...For You and Tomorrow's Generation by Josh McDowell (0-8054-9834-6) (LifeWay)

Truth Matters Leader Guide (0-8054-9833-8) (LifeWay)

The Five Love Languages of Children Video Pak by Gary Chapman and Ross Campbell (0-7673-3899-5) (LifeWay)

The Five Love Languages of Children Parent Activity Guide (0-7673-3898-7) (LifeWay)

New Faces in the Frame: A Guide to Marriage and Parenting in the Blended Family by Dick Dunn (0-8054-9817-6) (LifeWay)

Shaping the Next Generation by David and Elaine Atchison (0-7673-3476-0) (LifeWay)

Shaping the Next Generation Leader Kit (0-7673-3484-1) (LifeWay)

Magazines

HomeLife magazine (monthly)

ParentLife magazine (monthly for parents of newborns to 12-year-olds)

Living with Teenagers magazine (monthly for parents of youth)

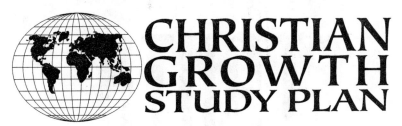

CHRISTIAN GROWTH STUDY PLAN

Preparing Christians to Serve

In the **Christian Growth Study Plan (formerly Church Study Course),** this book Parenting by Grace: Discipline & Spiritual Growth is a resource for course credit in the subject area Home/Family of the Christian Growth category of diploma plans. To receive credit, read the book, complete the learning activities, show your work to your pastor, a staff member or church leader, then complete the following information. This page may be duplicated. Send the completed page to:

Christian Growth Study Plan
127 Ninth Avenue, North, MSN 117
Nashville, TN 37234-0117
FAX: (615)251-5067

For information about the Christian Growth Study Plan, refer to the current Christian Growth Study Plan Catalog. Your church office may have a copy. If not, request a free copy from the Christian Growth Study Plan office (615/251-2525).

Parenting by Grace: Discipline & Spiritual Growth
COURSE NUMBER: CG- 0209

PARTICIPANT INFORMATION

Social Security Number (USA Only)

Personal CGSP Number*

Date of Birth (Mo., Day, Yr.)

Name (First, MI, Last)

☐Mr. ☐Miss
☐Mrs. ☐

Home Phone

Address (Street, Route, or P.O. Box)

City, State, or Province

Zip/Postal Code

CHURCH INFORMATION

Church Name

Address (Street, Route, or P.O. Box)

City, State, or Province

Zip/Postal Code

CHANGE REQUEST ONLY

☐Former Name

☐Former Address

City, State, or Province

Zip/Postal Code

☐Former Church

City, State, or Province

Zip/Postal Code

Signature of Pastor, Conference Leader, or Other Church Leader

Date

*New participants are requested but not required to give SS# and date of birth. Existing participants, please give CGSP# when using SS# for the first time.
Thereafter, only one ID# is required. *Mail To:* Christian Growth Study Plan, 127 Ninth Ave., North, MSN 117, Nashville, TN 37234-0117. Fax: (615)251-5067

TRUTH MATTERS...

FOR YOU AND TOMORROW'S GENERATION

by Josh McDowell

ADULT WORKBOOK

Truth Matters helps parents, church leaders, educators, and others better instill in children strong biblical values. Adults will apply absolute truth to everyday life choices and help pass to children the process for focusing on God's Word in response to ongoing moral challenges. This eight-session study for adults includes daily activities to complete between weekly sessions. ISBN 0805498346

LEADER GUIDE

Provides comprehensive administrative helps and easy-to-follow teaching procedures for leading adult group sessions. ISBN 0805498338

Order resources by writing to Customer Service Center, MSN 113; 127 Ninth Avenue, North; Nashville, TN 37234-0113; by calling toll free 1-800-458-2772; by faxing (615) 251-5933; or by emailing: customerservice@bssb.com.